# The Herb Handbook

# The Herb Handbook

## Su Bristow

ISLAND BOOKS

This edition published in 2004 by
S. WEBB & Son (Distributors) LTD
Telford Place, Pentraeth Road,
Menai Bridge,
Isle of Anglesey, LL59 5RW

© 2004 D&S Books Ltd

D&S Books Ltd
Kerswell,
Parkham Ash, Bideford
Devon, England
EX39 5PR

e-mail us at:-
enquiries@dsbooks.fsnet.co.uk

This edition printed 2004

ISBN 1-856578-97-2

DS0086. Herb Handbook

Creative Director: Sarah King
Editor: Sally MacEachern
Project editor: Anna Southgate
Photographer: Paul Forrester/Colin Bowling
Designer: Axis Design Editions
Illustrations: David Ashby

Fonts used within this book: Centaur and Gill Sans

Printed in China

1 3 5 7 9 10 8 6 4 2

# Contents

# INTRODUCTION

# What is a herb?

Years ago, when I was fairly new to the practice of herbal medicine, I was invited to give a talk about it, along with an acupuncturist and a homeopath. My slot was the last, and I listened while the acupuncturist gave an elegant explanation, illustrated with diagrams, of the Five Elements system in traditional Chinese medicine. Next came the homeopath, who talked of building up a picture of the patient through careful questions, a step-by-step process leading inevitably to the right remedy. You could even diagnose, he said, by means of a computer program.

In both cases, they seemed to be presenting an apparently foolproof method for defining the patient and selecting the appropriate treatment. Neither of them, of course, did full justice to their subject, but in giving such a cut-and-dried view of their respective disciplines, they had left me with quite a challenge.

For herbal medicine is messy. There are ancient and sophisticated systems for using herbs, there is straightforward first aid, there is wisdom and there is magic and

Herbs are easy to grow, no matter how small the space.

mumbo-jumbo. There are mysterious and exotic herbs from the Amazon rainforest, and there are weeds that are a nuisance in your garden. There is hard research into the active constituents of this plant or that extract, and there is what worked for your neighbour down the road. What there certainly is not is one all-embracing picture that can be said to describe herbal medicine.

Even defining a herb is not straightforward. In traditional Chinese medicine, for example, the pharmacopoeia includes quite a few mineral and animal products — including some very dodgy things like rhino horn and seahorses — as well as plants; anything is grist to the mill. In modern times, however, most reputable herbalists only use remedies of vegetable origin. But what makes a plant a herb? There is a teaching story from Tibet about an aged master herbalist who sent out his apprentice one morning, with instructions to return as soon as he had found a plant that had no medicinal action at all. The young man set off confidently, expecting an easy task. It was long after nightfall when he limped wearily home, empty-handed.

Pretty well any plant, then, has the

potential to be a herb. Even the blandest of foodstuffs, like rice or oats or carrots, has some action besides that of simply nourishing the body. It is certainly safe to say that all culinary herbs have some medicinal action, so you could define them as a special subset of herbs. We also call plants herbs when their virtues are not strictly medicinal, although they may enhance our wellbeing. These include the lovely scented herbs that we use to perfume our bodies, clothes and houses, and the not-so-lovely scents that help to repel insects and micro-organisms. Herbs can be strewn on the floor to soak up spills and smells, help preserve foods and add bite to alcoholic brews. Sacred herbs are used in ceremonies and magical herbs are vital ingredients for charms and amulets. Some herbs bring visions, while others banish them. Some herbs attract bees and butterflies to our gardens, and some simply delight our eyes.

How do we deal with all this chaotic abundance? The only answer must be to embrace it. I have now been in practice for more than 15 years, and for me the solution is a kind of dance. There are ways in which we can classify herbs — and people — and systems we can use, but always in the knowledge that there is more to it than that. Modern herbalists need to know the

Herb gardens come in many shapes and sizes.

traditional uses of leaf, bark, root and flower, and how they vary from country to country where they are used. They need to know the chemical components of the herb, and their actions on the body. They need to know the claims that are being made for them in the media, especially on the internet, and how to evaluate them. And they need to know the patient's hopes and fears. From all this, a picture will emerge that can then be combined with the herbs, and adjusted to the changing needs of the person taking them.

In other words, there are very few absolutes in herbal medicine. Even the plants themselves vary, not just in where they grow and the season of the year, but according to the time of day. And that is something not to worry about, but to celebrate. Unlike animals, plants take their nutrients directly from the earth and from sunlight. Without them animals, including humans, could not live. For that, they deserve our reverence, and our thanks.

Herbs to delight the eye...

# The herbs in this book

Out of all the possible millions of plants that have some healing powers, I have chosen 120 or so for this book. Not all of them are fashionable as healing herbs today, but they deserve a mention because of their importance in the past. They include strewing herbs like *Asperula odorata* (sweet woodruff) and magical herbs used in ceremonies. Some, like the vacciniums (cranberry and bilberry), have recently become fashionable as new uses are discovered for them. Quite a few are used more in cookery than in medicine.

Herbs cannot easily be separated from food. Some act on specific symptoms in the same way as drugs, but most have a broadly supportive action, nourishing and strengthening. Most of the herbs in this book fall into that category. All culinary herbs do more than just add flavour to a meal; they also help you to digest it. And if your digestion is working properly, so do many other functions of your body. The reverse is also true; an acid stomach or an irritable bowel may not seem to be related to other health problems, but they are both expressions of stress. If your relationship with food and with eating is not good, it affects your wellbeing in all sorts of ways, some subtle and some not so subtle. Herbs can help to heal this relationship.

When you take orthodox drugs, most of which are single chemical compounds, they are not received like food; they do not nourish you or enhance your digestion, and breaking them down takes energy. The same applies to food additives and many vitamin and mineral supplements. A whole herb extract, however, is no different from a food preparation, and the body receives

...and the nose as well.

it as such. We are designed to break food down, use what we need for nutrition, healing and repair, and expel residues. These are also essential to our digestion in that they provide roughage. This is why it is safe to combine most herbs with drugs. In fact, they will often help you cope better with the drugs, and can even be used to buffer some of their unwanted side effects. There are some exceptions, however, such as *Ginkgo* and *Hypericum*.

Herbs are useful as well as beautiful.

Most of the herbs mentioned in the book are entirely safe, and you can use them as much as you like. Where there is a need for caution, I have pointed it out, herb by herb. Some herbs are mainly used in healing, some more in cookery, and a few for other reasons, or simply because they are beautiful. I hope you will enjoy them as much as I do.

# What can herbs do for us?

The first and most basic action of most of the herbs in this book is to feed us, not just in the physical sense, but on the level of spirit as well. Quite simply, they enhance our vitality. They tend to have a tonic action, like a dose of sea air or a really good laugh; they wake us up and they get things moving. You can experience this directly with some of the more bitter-tasting herbs; when you take a mouthful of tincture, you may actually shudder as the taste hits you. Certainly saliva will start to flow, digestive juices in your stomach and intestines will be mobilised and your liver will be activated. Your system is awake and ready to deal with what comes next. There is an old saying that, 'If it tastes bad it must be good for you', and as far as these herbs are concerned, it is the simple truth.

So many of our problems, both physical and otherwise, start with some form of depletion. A lot of things draw on our resources – stress, illness, working continually, especially on repetitive or unrewarding tasks, not eating well, not exercising, drinking too much, not sleeping enough, not having enough fun. We all know how the list goes. What we are not so good at is replenishing ourselves. We tend to ignore the warning signs – tiredness, irritability, minor physical symptoms, and simply not enjoying life – until things have gone too far, and real problems begin to emerge. By that time, it can be quite a long road back to health.

Herbs can play a vital part in dealing with depletion. They can't make up for chronic lack of sleep, exercise or good food, and they can't give you sunshine and good companions and *joie de vivre*, but they can help to turn a vicious circle around, give you some ground to stand on and start to replace lost reserves. And when your life force is stronger, a lot of problems become easier to deal with, or they simply fall away. A vicious circle becomes a virtuous one. Then you are in a better position to make healthy choices, and steer your life in a more positive direction.

Their action, however, goes a lot further than that. Plants contain a vast range of compounds, some of which have specific actions, and many of which act in synergy. Some stimulate, and others soothe. Some act mainly on specific parts of the body, like *Taraxacum radix* for the liver, or *Crataegus oxyacanthoides* for the heart and circulation. Others, like *Panax ginseng*, are general life-enhancers, helping us to cope better with whatever is thrown at us. Whatever your question may be, there will be an answer somewhere in the plant world. That is not to say that herbs can cure everything. But there is nearly always

something they can do; where they cannot
cure, they can support you in coping with
the problem.

## WHEN TO USE THEM

All the herbs in the book are safe to use at
the dosages and in the ways described. If
there is a danger of possible interactions
with drugs or other treatments, I have
pointed this out. Do not be afraid to
experiment, within those limits. What
you will find is that there is a great deal
you can do on the level of first aid or
straightforward treatments that will
give fairly quick or instant results.
Beyond that, there is also plenty of
scope for improving the health of
various organs or systems and for
strengthening and supporting in all
sorts of ways. For example, an
anti-inflammatory herb like
*Matricaria recutita* (chamomile) can
help to heal a cut or sunburn on the
skin. Used continually over a period
of weeks or months, it can clear up
stomach ulcers and help prevent their reoccurrence. Likewise, you can use
*Rosmarinus officinalis* (rosemary) to ease a
headache, but if you take it every day, it
will help prevent headaches and migraines,

Chamomile: a
gentle healer.

Herbs provide a good 'show' for most of the year.

and sharpen up your concentration.

This does not mean that you have to take herbs all the time. All our lives, our systems work towards wholeness and health. When health breaks down, our main task is to find out what is causing the breakdown and then change it — our vital energy can do the rest. Herbs are our friends and allies, lending their vital energy to the task for as long as we need it.

The golden rule in self-treatment should always be: if you don't get results within a reasonable period of time, seek professional help, whether in the form of a medical herbalist, a doctor or some other complementary therapist. If you are taking herbs for a long-term problem, as a general rule, you should get a sense that things are moving in the right direction within two to three months. If they are not, either something is getting in the way, or some other treatment is needed. Likewise, if you are unsure, if the picture is complicated or if you feel out of your depth, ask an expert. Sometimes you need another person's healing energy, as well as

his or her knowledge and experience. The way to health lies through connectedness — with our own body wisdom, with the world around us and with other people. Sometimes, knowing that we can't do it on our own is the first step towards recovery.

Rosemary for remembrance.

Herbs are essential to the cottage garden.

# Chapter 1

# GATHERING AND STORING HERBS

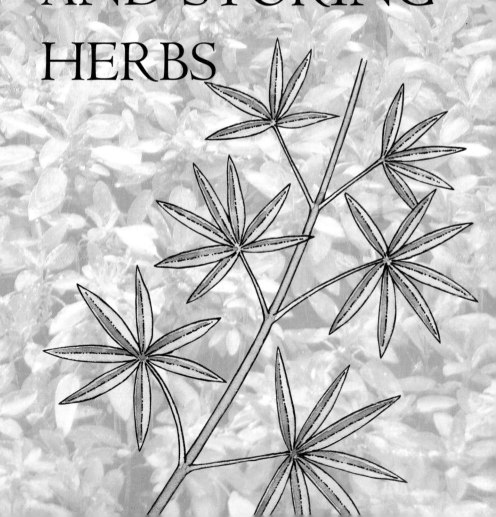

# Gathering and storing herbs

Many herbal remedies include wildflowers, or garden weeds, that are so common they are entirely safe to collect. Others are not so secure, and in some countries there are laws about digging up roots or even picking the leaves of wild plants. Please be respectful, and do not do anything to threaten the continued existence of these precious allies. Many popular herbs, like *Panax ginseng*, *Hydrastis canadensis* (golden seal) and *Cypripedium pubescens* (lady's slipper), have been gathered almost to extinction in their native habitats. Don't use them unless you know they have been cultivated rather than gathered in the wild.

Many remedies from developing

Ginseng: a herbal powerhouse

Hydrastis has been almost gathered to extinction in the wild.

countries may also be over-harvested as demand from the richer areas of the world pushes up the price. Fragile habitats can be damaged, local economies upset, and the continued existence of the remedy itself placed in jeopardy. Use herbs responsibly; there may be an invisible price tag on exotic plants with mysterious healing powers. Nearly always, there will be something just as good, if not better, growing much closer to home.

Monarda didyma: a refreshing digestive.

# Growing your own

Wherever you live, it will be possible to grow at least a few herbs, if only on a windowsill. Growing herbs is a very good way to develop a working relationship. If the herbs you choose already grow wild in the area, they will need very little attention, and may even start to crowd out the less robust inhabitants of your garden. Non-native plants will be happiest if you can provide them with living conditions as close as possible to those in which they naturally thrive. For example, many of our favourite culinary herbs, such as *Thymus, Salvia, Rosmarinus* and *Origanum*, originally come from the Mediterranean. They do best, and produce the most intensely scented leaves, in the dry, sunny, well-drained conditions of their home environment.

Under each herb, where appropriate, I have given brief notes about how to grow it and when to harvest it. This is not a comprehensive guide to cultivation, but will provide a useful starting point.

Oregano makes food both tastier and more digestible.

# Herb gathering

The best way to get to know wild plants is to go out exploring with someone who has already trodden the path. There's no substitute, and no more satisfying way to learn, than to spend time with someone who knows – and loves – plants. So if you know a herbalist, or a plant enthusiast, tag along. If you don't, look out for someone advertising a herb walk or a class about herbal medicine. Books and other teaching aids are essential, of course, but there's no substitute for person-to-person handing down of knowledge. That's the way herbal knowledge has been passed down through the centuries.

Always make sure you know what you are gathering.

That said, you must have a good flora, and learn to identify plants with confidence before you try them out on yourself or anybody else. A lot of plants will do nothing for your health, and some are very definitely harmful. Our ancestors sorted out the business of trial and error a long time ago, and we don't need to go over that ground again. You'll soon discover that the same plant can look very different depending on where it is growing, the time of year and its state of

Use a reliable flora…

health, but you'll also develop the ability to recognise it under any conditions. Most plants are pretty distinctive, just like animals, once you get the eye for it.

When it comes to gathering herbs to use as remedies, the key is to choose plants that are as healthy as possible. You are asking that plant to share its vitality with you, so don't pick specimens that look as though they are in trouble, or are growing too near a road or some other source of pollution. And when you do find what you want, don't be greedy; leave enough for that colony to thrive.

## WHEN TO GATHER

In tropical and subtropical areas, the best time of year for different parts of a plant will vary. However, plants that grow in temperate zones tend to grow fast in spring, flower in summer, set fruit or seed in autumn and die back, or at least slow down, in winter. Accordingly, if you want to gather leaves and stems, you'll find them at their peak in spring and early summer before the flowers appear. Picking off buds before they can flower will

...Or ask an expert.

*Urtica*: one of our most versatile herbs.

prolong your harvest of leaves. If you're a fan of nettle (*Urtica dioica*) soup, for example, a little judicious pruning of your nettle crop should keep you in tender young greens for most of the year.

Flowers are best picked just as they begin to open. Seeds should be gathered when they are ripe and ready to fall. Late autumn and winter or early spring are the times for digging roots, when the vitality of the plant has sunk beneath the earth.

## Phases of the moon

Plants, like all other living things, are largely water, and so they respond to the pull of the moon. Seeds germinate better if you sow them in the few days before the moon is full. It's not easy to quantify, but the potency of the aerial parts of a plant — leaves, stems, flowers and seeds — is likely to be greater when the moon is waxing, whereas the root will be at its best at new moon. This is less important for medicinal than for magical purposes, but the dividing line between the two has always been hazy.

## Time of day

The chemical constituents of a plant change subtly from hour to hour — a fact that plagues the quality controllers, but inspires reverence in the respectful herbalist. The aerial parts are at their best in the morning, after the dew has dried and before the sun has burnt off too much moisture. Roots come into their own in the evening and at night.

## Weather conditions

Try not to gather leaves and flowers when they are wet, simply because they are harder to dry and more likely to develop moulds. Intense sunlight will decrease the amount of precious volatile oils in your sample.

Having said that, you are most likely to go gathering when you have the time, and when it isn't raining. Ideal conditions are something to aim for, but not to get too hung up on. The will to do it is more important than getting it exactly right.

# Storing your herbs

The usual way to preserve what you collect is by drying. Roots and stems need to be washed and cut up before drying; it is almost impossible afterwards. Do not wash leaves and flowers, as the moisture will encourage the growth of moulds. Shake off any dust or insects.

The aim is to dry the herbs as quickly, but as gently, as possible. Drying in direct sunlight is too harsh for a lot of herbs, especially those with a high volatile oil content. The ideal place in most households is on the slatted shelves in the airing cupboard, laid out on sheets of paper, with the door open so that air can circulate. Probably the worst thing you can do is to hang up your herbs in decorative bunches above the stove. They attract grease, dust and insects, bits drop off and they are at the mercy of sunlight and heat.

Fresh *Taraxacum* root: clean it and chop into small pieces.

They may convince your neighbours that you're a healer, but they won't do much for your patients.

Drying should be finished in two to three days. If dried well, the leaves and flowers will be crisp and will crumble at your touch, but their colour should be bright and their scent, if any, fresh and

Wash freshly dug roots and chop them up before drying.

strong. So where to keep them? Once again, the prettiest option is the worst. Herbs sealed in clear glass jars and kept near the stove or on the windowsill will very soon be useless except for feeding the compost heap. Although they are dried, they still contain a fair amount of water, and in a sealed container condensation and moulds will develop. They will fare best in plain brown paper bags – clearly labelled with the name of the herb, the part collected and the date – stored somewhere cool and out of direct sunlight. Stored like this, they should keep for at least a year.

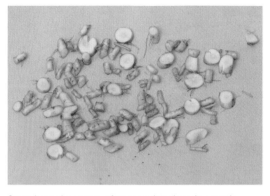

Spread out the pieces of root so that they dry evenly.

Dried herbs: *Artemisia absinthinium*.

*Artemisia dracunculus* (tarragon); dry the fresh herbs.

Bottle, store and label your preparations carefully.

# Preparing herbs

Herbal medicine involves a great deal of cookery. In the old days, when most of the remedies people used were grown, gathered or bought (expensively) from an apothecary, this was an integral part of the healing process. As you pound, chop, mix, simmer and strain, so you add your own healing intention to the brew. Most traditional practitioners from any of the world's major systems of medicine would agree that this is at least as important as any of the physical ingredients. It isn't possible to compare the efficacy of a home-grown, home-made prescription with a bottle of factory-made tablets bought off the shelf, because the herbal prescription would be individually tailored to the patient, and the ingredients would vary according to the practitioner's judgment, the time of year, and what was available locally.

Nowadays we have to rely, to some extent, on mass-produced and pre-packaged remedies, but there is still plenty of scope for creativity. Even if you are only making a cup of herb tea from a box of teabags, you can still bring your positive intentions to the process. Our forebears developed a huge array of recipes for herbal remedies, both internal and external, and the scope is potentially endless. I have chosen just a few, all tried and tested, which are well within the scope of the average kitchen. And once you have the basic principles, you can go on to develop your own.

You might think that the best way of taking herbs would be to eat or use them fresh, without any preparation at all. Sometimes this is true. *Tanacetum parthenium* (feverfew), for example, is most powerful eaten fresh, and five leaves are enough. On the whole, though, preparation delivers the herbs more effectively. There are several reasons for this. One is that the amount of herb you would need to eat for a medicinal dose is often quite high and even if it didn't taste bitter, it would

be quite difficult to get it down. To get a useful sedative effect from lettuce, for example, you would need to eat a whole one. Preparation concentrates the active ingredients, and leaves behind some of the inert parts of the plant, like cellulose.

Another reason is that preparation begins the process of digestion. This is why we can eat more cooked food than raw, and why cooked food is sometimes easier to digest. A sick person needs to concentrate their energies on getting well, and their digestion may be in need of support, so it makes sense to introduce remedies as gently as possible, in a way that can easily be taken up. Someone with

*Tanacetum parthenium* can help with migraines and arthritis.

Recipes use dried herbs. This is elderflower.

they will be available whenever you want them. Just as preserving food has enabled people to live in places where fresh food is not always available, so making remedies extends our healing power.

The quantities of herb given in the following recipes are always for dried herb, partly because fresh herb is not always available, and partly because it contains a variable amount of water, which would affect the finished product. As a rule of thumb, fresh herb contains about four times as much water as dried, so if you use it, you will need to adjust the recipes accordingly.

A herbal teas are an extremely pleasant way to enjoy the benefits of herbs.

stomach ulcers or an irritable bowel, for example, will not absorb raw food as easily as cooked.

A third reason is practicality; preparing things also preserves them, and means that

## HERB TEAS

A herb tea is simply an extract of herb in water, usually hot. For leaves and flowers, it is enough to pour boiling water over them and leave the tea to brew for about five minutes. This is called an infusion. For tough stems and roots, stronger measures are needed. Put them in water and boil them for about 15 minutes to make a decoction (or 'soup' in the Chinese

### To make an infusion

Ingredients for elderflower tea

Put the dried herb into a teapot. Two heaped teaspoonfuls is usually enough.

Add half a litre of boiling water, stir and let it infuse for five minutes.

Strain and drink hot.

system). For both methods you need about 30g of dried herb (or 120g of fresh herb) to half a litre of water to make a standard medicinal extract. Don't worry about exact measures. Dosage is not that critical with any of the herbs in this book, except where specifically mentioned. You can experiment with the strength of your tea to make it more (or less) palatable, as you like. You can mix herbs together, add lemon or a pinch of cinnamon or ginger, or even try to disguise the taste with fruit juice. The ideal dose is two to three cups of tea daily.

The aromatic herbs are especially good to take as teas; they are pleasant to drink and will have an instantly relaxing effect.

Boiling herbs for a decoction.

They are most often used as digestives, and as a quick way to reduce nervous tension – or to pep you up, like coffee and other caffeine-containing herbs. A tea can also be used as a wash or lotion on the skin, or added to a bath. Once made, an infusion or decoction will keep, if refrigerated, for up to 24 hours.

## To make a decoction
Put 30g dried herb (roots, stalks or seeds) into a saucepan, and add about 750ml water. Bring to the boil and simmer for 15 minutes. Strain before using.

### TINCTURES
These are a modern invention, usually made with a mixture of water and alcohol

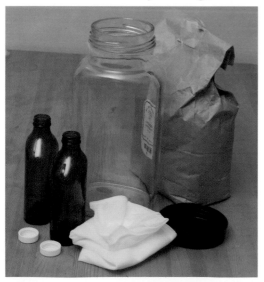
Everything you need for making tinctures.

## To make a tincture

**You will need:**

- A big sealable glass container (a 2-litre sweet jar is ideal)
- A fine muslin cloth or bag (bags are sold for winemaking)
- Dark glass bottles
- Labels

**Ingredients:**

240g dried herb
1l vodka

Put the dried herb and vodka into the jar and seal it.

Shake well. Then let it stand, somewhere out of direct sunlight, for two weeks, shaking or turning it daily.

At the end of that time, strain off the tincture into a bowl.

Make sure you squeeze out all the liquid.

Pour into dark glass bottles. Label it with the date and name of the herb or herbs you have used.

or glycerol. Alcohol is the favourite. It is a superb extractor of the active ingredients of most plants, so that your dose of medicine comes in a teaspoon rather than a cup (good news with some of the stronger tasting herbs). Also, tinctures keep for a year or more, unlike teas. Obviously, they are not suitable for recovering alcoholics, or anyone with a sensitivity or an aversion to alcohol, but

Always measure dosage carefully.

for everyone else they do very well. Vodka, at 30% alcohol (60 proof), contains the right proportion of alcohol to water for most herbs.

## Dosage

The standard adult dosage is three 5ml teaspoonfuls of tincture daily, usually on an empty stomach. For people over 70 and under 7, halve the dosage, and for babies a few drops can be enough. It is hard to be precise because some people seem to need bucketfuls to have any effect, and some are sensitive to minute doses. On the whole, the person taking the remedy is the best judge.

Syrups are a lovely way of preparing fruits and berries.

## SYRUPS

One of the older ways to preserve herbal extracts, as well as fruits and juices, is by making a syrup with sugar. You could also use honey or maple syrup, but you would need to adjust the proportions of the recipe to allow for the higher water content. Syrups are especially useful for cough medicine, when you need it to slip down slowly, working its magic on the way. Use herbs that are rich in mucilage, like *Althaea radix* (marshmallow), *Viola odorata* (sweet violet) or *Symphytum officinale* (comfrey) leaf, and the syrup will be so thick it will hardly pour out of the pan. Syrups help to disguise the taste of the herbs, which can be helpful if you are giving them to children, or to adults who make a fuss. It is better not to resort to 'sweetening the pill' if you can avoid it, but if the choice is between that or not taking the remedy at all, then there is a case to be made.

Some fruits, like elderberries (*Sambucus nigra*) and rosehips (*Rosa canina*) are rich in vitamin C. A syrup made from them can be diluted with hot water to make a warming winter drink to ward off colds. Add some nutmeg (*Myristica fragrans*) or cinnamon (*Cinnamonum zeylanicum*) and you will have a lovely non-alcoholic fruit cup.

## To make a syrup:

**You will need:**
- Saucepan
- Muslin for straining
- Measuring jug
- Rubber gloves
- Wooden spoon
- Dark glass bottles
- Labels

First make an infusion or a decoction of the herb. If the herb is rich in mucilage, a cold infusion will give you the best results — simply soak the herb in cold water for 12 hours. For example, 30g *Althaea* root soaked in 400ml of cold water should yield about 300ml of cold infusion after straining.

The proportion of sugar to water must be 65% to 35%, or the syrup will not keep for very long. For 300ml of infused herb, for example, add 600g sugar. Warm the mixture over a low heat until the sugar has dissolved, then let it cool. Strain and bottle.

## INFUSED OIL

Extracting the essential oil from a herb is an industrial process, beyond the scope of domestic resources, but you can easily make an infused oil. This can be used as a lotion, poured onto a compress or added to a poultice. It is also a first step towards making a cream.

To make a cold infusion, simply soak the herb in cold oil.

### To make an infused oil:

**You will need:**
- Bain-marie or double boiler (for hot infusions)
- Wooden spoon
- 2-litre glass jar with sealable lid
- Muslin bag, or cloth, for straining
- Rubber gloves
- Dark glass bottles
- Labels

You can use any vegetable oil as a base, although a light one without a strong flavour of its own is best; sunflower, grapeseed or almond oil are favourites. There are three methods:

### 1. Cold infusion

For herbs like *Symphytum*, which is high in valuable mucilage that would be destroyed by heat, or for herbs so full of essential oil that they give it up readily, like *Allium sativum*, a cold infusion works best. Put a litre of oil into the glass jar, add enough herb to make a thick porridge-like mixture, and leave for a few weeks, shaking it daily. Strain out the herb through muslin, bottle and label the oil.

### 2. Sun infusion

This is the traditional method for *Hypericum*, which yields a red oil that is very valuable for treating burns and muscular strains. The method works well – as long as there is enough sun – for many other herbs, but not for those that are high in volatile oils because these are

fragile and may degrade in the sun. Simply put the herb and oil into the jar and stand it in the sun for about six weeks, shaking or turning it daily. Then strain and bottle the oil. For extra strength, you can add more herb to the oil and infuse it again.

For a sun infusion, shake the jar daily.

A hot infusion is made by heating the mixture over boiling water

## 3. Hot infusion

If you are short of time, or sunshine, a hot infusion is the answer. Put the herb and oil into the top of the bain-marie (the oil must not be heated directly, or you will end up with fried herbs), and fill the bottom with water. Bring to the boil, cover and simmer for 2 hours, stirring from time to time. Strain out the herb from the oil, then add more herb and repeat the process. Pour into dark glass bottles, seal and label.

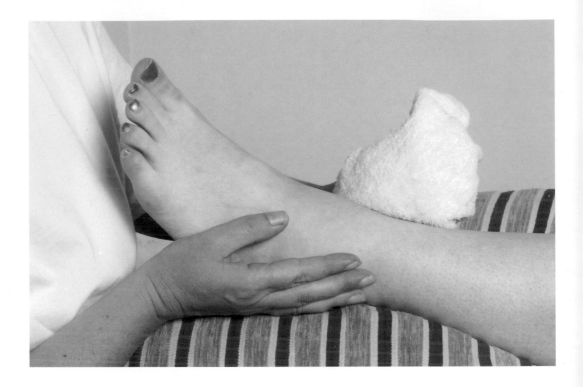

A poultice can be very soothing for a sprain.

## POULTICES

A poultice is an excellent way to apply herbs to the skin. The herbs can be fresh (bruised to release the active principles) or, more often, dried herbs made into a paste with hot water or oil. First, apply a little oil to the skin to prevent the poultice from sticking. Take a piece of thin cloth – muslin, gauze or even an old flannel will do – and spread the herbal paste on it. Lay another cloth over the herb, and fold in the edges to prevent leakage. Place the poultice directly on the skin. To keep the heat and to enhance the healing action, cover the poultice with a hot-water bottle.

Poultices are very soothing for inflamed muscles and joints. They can also ease pain – after an operation, around the area of a tumour, or during menstruation. Use herbs, such as *Zingiber* root, *Rosmarinus*, *Juniperus* or *Brassica*, that bring heat to the area and soothe spasm. Herbs such as

*Thymus* or *Eucalyptus* can be put on the chest to ease congestion and help mucus to clear. Herbs such as *Symphytum* root, *Althaea* root or oatmeal can be very useful to soothe and moisturise the skin in bouts of eczema. Finally, try a poultice to draw an abscess or a boil or to get foreign bodies and pus out of a wound. Old favourites for this include *Linum* and *Ulmus fulva*.

## CREAMS AND OINTMENTS

For a preparation that will stay on the skin, you need a cream base. What you use as a base depends on what you want the cream to do. If you want it to act as a barrier – for hands exposed to harsh detergents, for instance – or to carry the active ingredients without disappearing too quickly – a chest rub to help an asthmatic patient to breathe, perhaps – then the base must not be soluble in water. The technical term for this type of preparation is an ointment. On the other hand, if you want a light cream that will be quickly taken up, the base must be largely water-soluble. In practice, a useful base will be a mixture that is fairly solid in the jar, but melts quickly into the skin when it is applied. The following is a quick run-through of some of the more popular bases.

Traditional bases such lard, butter or other animal fats were the mainstay of

Equipment for making a cream.

home-made remedies until recent times, but they do not keep very long and are unacceptable to vegetarians and vegans. Nowadays, there are mineral-based alternatives such as vaseline or other petroleum-derived products. They keep well, but often contain preservatives that can irritate sensitive skin. A natural choice is a vegetable oil. Some, like sunflower or grapeseed oil, are neutral carriers, while others bring their own qualities to the product. If you want your cream to be moisturising, for example, you could use avocado oil or coconut oil in the base. If you want it to be anti-inflammatory, some evening primrose oil would be useful.

Whatever oils you choose, they must be combined with something more solid so that you end up with a cream or ointment. The usual choices are beeswax (for non-vegans) or cocoa butter, and the more of either you add, the more heavy and long-lasting your preparation will be. The finishing touch is to add a few drops of some essential oil, which will help to preserve the final product, and also add their own medicinal action to it. Lavender oil, for example, will enhance the anti-inflammatory action of the cream, while thyme or ti-tree oil will give it extra anti-infective action.

Store your prepared creams in dark glass jars.

# To make a cream or an ointment

**You will need:**
- Bain-marie, or double boiler
- Wooden spoon
- Muslin cloth, or straining bag
- Rubber gloves
- Measuring jug
- Glass pots with tops
- Labels

## A quick ointment

Put 200g vaseline in the bain-marie, and bring the water underneath to the boil. Add two tablespoonfuls of dried herb, and simmer for about 10 minutes. Strain through the muslin into a jug, and pour into pots before it sets.

## Basic ointment
- 50g beeswax
- 450g olive oil
- 350g dried herb

Melt the beeswax and olive oil in the bain-marie. Add the dried herb, and infuse it gently for 2–3 hours. Strain through muslin and pour into pots before it sets.

If you like, you can add a few drops of essential oil after straining. For example, *Calendula* ointment would be enhanced by oil of *Thymus* or *Melaleuca* (Ti-tree) and *Symphytum* would go well with *Lavandula*. This ointment is good for sensitive skin.

## Cream
- 100g beeswax
- 200g cocoa butter
- 300g infused oil
- 270ml glycerol
- 330ml water
- 120g dried herb

Melt the beeswax, cocoa butter and infused oil base (see recipe above) in the bain-marie, and add the other ingredients. Heat them together for 2–3 hours. Make sure that all the water has evaporated, or the cream will not keep so well. Strain through muslin and pour into pots. Again, you can add some essential oil before the cream has set. By varying the proportions of base ingredients, and by using more or less glycerol, you can change the consistency of the final product.

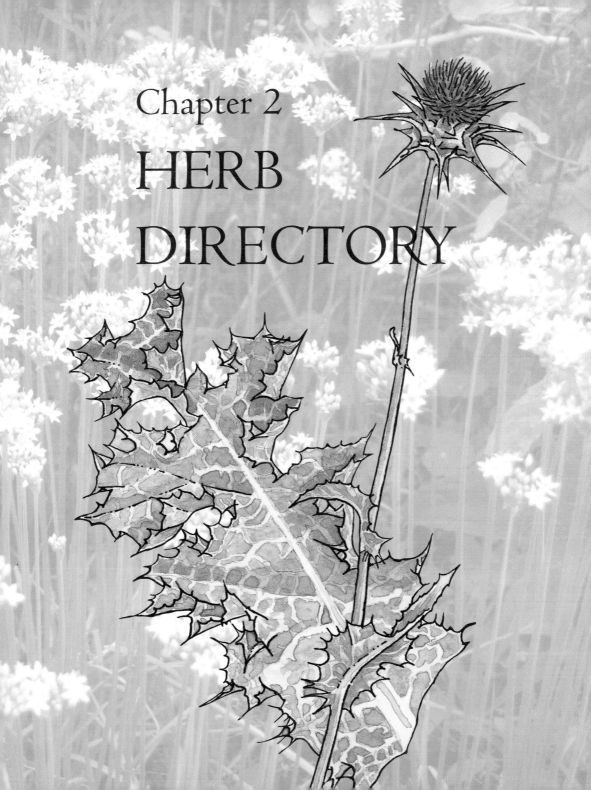

Chapter 2

# HERB

# DIRECTORY

# HOW TO USE THE HERB DIRECTORY

You will find here a pot-pourri of herbs. Many of them have other uses as well. In each case, the primary uses are indicated by the symbols at the top of the page, but the idea is to give you the 'flavour' of each herb.

I have also included notes on their common names in English, their family names and their countries of origin, so that you can find out more about the herbs if you wish. Where appropriate, I have given some guidance about how to grow them, although you will see that a good many medicinal herbs are still gathered from the wild. Finally, I have included a few notes on 'cautions' in cases where there are any restrictions on the use of a particular herb, or it is best used under professional guidance. notes on 'cautions' in cases where there are any restrictions on the use of a particular herb, or it is best used under professional guidance.

## KEY TO SYMBOLS

| | medicinal | | perfume | | cleaning agent |
|---|---|---|---|---|---|
| | culinary | | craft | | Christmas |

# ACHILLEA MILLEFOLIUM

Named after the Greek hero, Achilles, *Achillea* brings out the warrior in those who take it. It is a spine-stiffener, a useful ally when you are facing a difficult or daunting task.

There are two main medicinal uses for *Achillea*. Both stem from its ability to cause peripheral blood vessels to dilate. In other words, it warms up the hands, feet and skin, and tends to cool down the core of the body. This is very useful in the management of fever. Rather than suppressing the fever that goes with flu, chest infections and the like, which is what happens when you take aspirin or paracetamol, *Achillea* helps your body's natural effort to deal with infection by producing a sweat. *Achillea* works well in combination with herbs like *Sambucus*, *Mentha piperita* or *Zingiber* in this context.

The herb's second use is to bring down high blood pressure. Used as part of a long-term management strategy, it can help to normalise the blood pressure without the need for drugs, especially when taken, for example, with *Crataegus* or *Tilia*.

**FAMILY:**
*Compositae*

**COMMON ENGLISH NAMES:**
*Yarrow, milfoil*

**ORIGIN:**
*Europe, North Africa*

**MAIN USES:**
*Medicinal*

**PARTS USED:**
*Aerial parts*

## Culinary

In parts of Scandinavia, *Achillea* has been used as an ingredient in brewing beer, both for its fresh taste and for its ability to chase away bad moods.

## Other

In the I Ching, the Chinese system of divination now used all over the world, dried yarrow stalks are sorted in a particular way to arrive at a reading.

## Cultivation

Yarrow is a common wayside and grassland weed, flowering from June until about October.

# AESCULUS HIPPOCASTANUM

*A*esculus contains a combination of ingredients that help to strengthen and tone the walls of blood vessels, especially the veins. It is helpful for various venous problems, such as varicose veins, haemorrhoids and phlebitis. *Aesculus* combines well with *Achillea*, *Crataegus* or *Tilia*, and works best when used in short bursts of six weeks or so, with breaks of a few months in between.

This is a bracing herb, restoring tone where things have become lax. Because *Aesculus* is rich in tannins, it can be useful in gastritis, but should be used with caution by those with weak digestions. Take it with a soothing digestive like *Matricaria*, *Althaea* or *Glycyrrhiza* to offset this effect.

## Other

Children have played with conkers for many generations. They can be used like marbles, or strung on string and hit against each other.

## Cultivation

*Aesculus* is now widely grown in temperate areas. The fruits ripen in the northern hemisphere in September and October. They do not need drying if you collect them when fully ripe, but they will need to be cut up or grated before being made into tea, tincture or cream. Every child knows how hard conkers become as they age.

FAMILY:

*Hippocastanaceae*

COMMON ENGLISH NAMES:

*Horse chestnut, conker*

ORIGIN:

*Northern and Central Asia*

MAIN USES:

*Medicinal*

PARTS USED:

*Fruit, or conker*

# AGROPYRON REPENS

The primary use for *Agropyron* is in the treatment of urinary problems. It soothes inflammation, is gently diuretic, and discourages infectious organisms. It is particularly useful in dealing with cystitis, urethritis and prostatitis, but it can also be used both to treat acute infections and to discourage them in people who are prone to recurrent infections or irritability of the bladder and urethra. *Agropyron* combines well with *Arctostaphylos*, *Echinacea* and *Zea*.

## Cultivation

*Agropyron* is a pest to farmers and gardeners. Its creeping rhizomes grow fast and deep, are almost impossible to get rid of and compete very unfairly with whatever you are actually trying to grow. The thin, white underground stems are easily found if you lift a tuft of *Agropyron* with a garden fork. Lift and dry them in spring or early autumn.

| FAMILY: |
| --- |
| *Graminaceae* |

| COMMON ENGLISH NAMES: |
| --- |
| *Couch grass, twitch grass* |

| ORIGIN: |
| --- |
| *Very widespread* |

| MAIN USES: |
| --- |
| *Medicinal* |

| PARTS USED: |
| --- |
| *Rhizomes* |

# ALCHEMILLA ARVENSIS

The English name of *Alchemilla arvensis* is a corruption of parsley pierce-stone, which refers to its traditional use in the removal of kidney and bladder stones. Before the days of safe surgery, this was a highly prized virtue, and it is still valuable today for its health-promoting actions on the urinary system. In other words, even if stones can be removed, the conditions in which they formed will still need treating. *Alchemilla arvensis* helps in any case of painful urination or water retention, and can be combined with *Parietaria*, *Agropyron* or *Zea*, for example.

## Culinary

*Alchemilla arvensis* used to be a salad herb in the Middle Ages and has not (as yet) come back into fashion. It is astringent, but can be used with milder salads to add bite.

## Cultivation

It is a common wild plant below 500 metres, favouring dry soil and waste ground. Collect aerial parts in summer when the plant is in flower.

**FAMILY:**
Rosaceae

**COMMON ENGLISH NAMES:**
Parsley piert

**ORIGIN:**
Europe, North Africa; introduced into North America

**MAIN USES:**
Medicinal

**PARTS USED:**
Aerial parts

# ALCHEMILLA VULGARIS

Them herb's Latin name reflects the high regard in which the alchemillas were held; their actions were thought to be due to some kind of alchemical transformation. *Alchemilla vulgaris* helps to control heavy menstrual bleeding. It is tonic to the womb and associated tissues, so that problems with painful or heavy periods and the changes that come with the menopause are eased. Its soothing, anti-inflammatory action is useful in the management of conditions such as endometriosis and pelvic inflammatory disease as part of a wider programme of treatment. It can be combined with many other herbs, depending on the individual being treated. The shape of the leaves gives the herb its English name, which evokes the image of a gentle, all-enveloping mantle that enfolds and contains.

**FAMILY:**
*Rosaceae*

**COMMON ENGLISH NAMES:**
*Lady's mantle*

**ORIGIN:**
*Northern Europe and mountainous areas further south.*

**MAIN USES:**
*Medicinal*

**PARTS USED:**
*Leaves and flowering shoots*

Velvet cloaks for ladies.

## Caution

Heavy periods should not be allowed to go on too long, as they may eventually lead to anaemia and their underlying causes may need investigation. If self-medication has not helped enough after two or three menstrual cycles, consult a doctor or a professional herbalist, or both.

## Cultivation

A common weed, *Alchemilla vulgaris* can be grown easily in Northern Europe. It favours moist, upland habitats, spreads easily and is not fussy about conditions, as long as it is not too dry. Gardeners like *Alchemilla vulgaris* for its softly furred leaves, which hold drops of water after a rain shower. Collect leaves and flowering shoots between July and August.

# ALLIUM
# SATIVUM

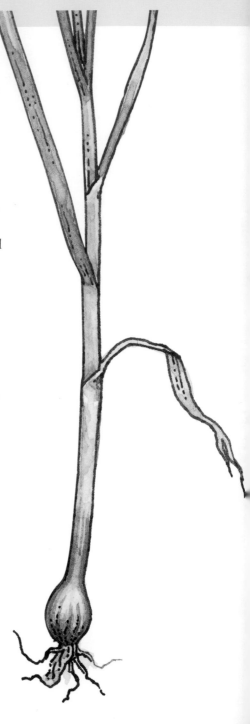

*A*llium sativum is a powerhouse. Taken in winter, it
is like a package of concentrated sunshine,
boosting your circulation and helping to drive out
the cold and damp. It will ward off infections of all
sorts, as the pungent oil is effective against bacterial,
viral and fungal infections, and it is particularly
useful for people who are prone to coughs, colds and
chest infections. It also helps to kill off infections,
from tummy bugs to parasites. Before the advent of
antibiotics, *A. sativum* was one of our main weapons
in dealing with this type of illness, and it is being
researched today for its ability to deal with some of
the antibiotic-resistant superbugs that lurk in
hospital wards.

    *A. sativum's* other great virtue lies in its action in

**FAMILY:**

*Alliaceae*

**COMMON ENGLISH NAMES:**

*Garlic*

**ORIGIN:**

*Europe; now widely cultivated*

**MAIN USES:**

*culinary*

**PARTS USED:**

*Corms*

the blood, for it lowers cholesterol and so helps prevent and treat arteriosclerosis and high blood pressure. At the same time, it reduces blood clotting, which gives it a valuable role to play in the prevention of strokes, and recovery after having one.

## Culinary

*A. sativum* not only helps to cleanse the digestive system, but also stimulates the release of digestive juices, so you make better use of your food. Although its pungent taste and smell can be overpowering, in small amounts it enhances the flavours of other foods. As a result, *A. sativum* is used in many types of cuisine around the world.

## Caution

If you are taking blood-thinning medications, such as aspirin or warfarin, check with your doctor before taking *A. sativum*, since you may need to reduce the dose of the drugs.

## Cultivation

*Allium sativum* likes a hot, dry climate and a well-drained, well-fed soil, but sunshine is its prime requirement. In the northern hemisphere, sow individual cloves in autumn, and lift and dry the bulbs in late summer, when the leaves are dying back. They should keep for a few months if you store them in a cool dry place.

# ALLIUM CEPA

*A*llium cepa has useful antiseptic properties. It is less powerful than *Allium sativum* in this regard, but also less pungent. A syrup made by steeping chopped onion in honey is a good cough and cold medicine for children. *Allium cepa* is also famous for its ability to promote the flow of mucus. The irritating quality that makes you cry when you cut up onions can be a blessing when you take them medicinally; gently but firmly, it will encourage blocked sinuses and inflamed respiratory tissues to free themselves up, as well as discouraging whatever infections may be contributing to these problems. Like *Allium sativum*, it combines well with *Sambucus, Achillea* or *Echinacea.*

**FAMILY:**

*Alliaceae*

**COMMON ENGLISH NAMES:**

*Onion*

**ORIGIN:**

*Now worldwide*

**MAIN USES:**

*Culinary*

**PARTS USED:**

*Swollen bulb at base of stem*

## Culinary

Food is warmed by the addition of onions, so that other flavours are brought out. Their presence encourages digestive juices to flow, so that you make better use of the food you eat.

## Caution

*A. cepa* can be unsuitable for some people with irritable conditions of the intestine.

## Cultivation

Onions are easy to grow. They like a well-tilled soil and a fairly dry growing season. They are lifted and dried when the stems die down in late summer.

# ALLIUM SCHOENOPRASUM

This is the smallest of the allium family. The snipped leaves are used to garnish many dishes from salads – where they add a touch of fire – to richer foods like eggs, cheese and meat – where they give a counterpoint to fats.

## Cultivation

Chives are easily grown, and spread by dividing clumps in autumn. Cut the leaves when they are up to 20 centimetres or so. Although the flower-heads are very decorative, removing them will prolong the production of useful leaves until the first frosts.

FAMILY:
*Alliaceae*

COMMON ENGLISH NAMES:
*Chives*

ORIGIN:
*Northern Europe*

MAIN USES:
*Culinary*

PARTS USED:
*Leaves*

# ALOE VERA AND SPECIES

*A*loe is an essential ingredient of any herbal first-aid kit. Used externally, it is a soothing and cooling wound healer. It takes the heat out of sunburn or minor burns, and re-moisturises the skin at the same time. Insect bites, stings, grazes and mild eczema respond well, especially if *Aloe* is combined with some *Calendula* tea or tincture for its antiseptic properties. Aloe also works well with *Hypericum* and *Symphytum*.

Internally, its main traditional use was as a powerful purgative, for in its unprocessed state it contains some strongly laxative ingredients. However, this use is best left to the professionals, as it needs to be carefully combined with carminatives — herbs that relax the muscles of the stomach and intestines — to avoid uncomfortable griping. Such herbs might include *Carum carvi, Matricaria chamomilla, Zingiber officinalis* or *Mentha piperita.*

**FAMILY:**
*Liliaceae*

**COMMON ENGLISH NAMES:**
*Aloe*

**ORIGIN:**
*East and South Africa; now widely cultivated*

**MAIN USES:**
*Medicinal*

**PARTS USED:**
*Juice or gel from the leaves*

With the purgative ingredients removed, *Aloe* has become one of the biggest-selling herbal products of recent years. Without the purgatives, *Aloe* is just as effective at healing wounds and soothing inflammation inside the body as out. It is an excellent remedy for irritable bowel, colic and the aftermath of intestinal infections of all sorts. *Aloe* is very useful in the management of conditions such as Crohn's disease and ulcerative colitis – in conjunction, of course, with expert guidance. It can also be helpful in calming rheumatoid arthritis. There are many other claims made for it, but these are its main areas of action.

## Caution

*Aloe* for internal use cannot be prepared at home from the raw plant, but there are many reliable products available on the market.

## Cultivation

Aloes are succulents, thriving in a hot, dry climate. In areas where they will not grow outdoors, they are easy to keep as pot plants. They grow fast and are easily divided. When you need some *Aloe* juice to treat an insect bite, burn or sunburn, for example, you can simply break off a leaf and apply the fresh juice to the skin.

# ALTHAEA OFFICINALIS

*A*lthaea officinalis is rich in mucilage, a kind of sticky juice or gel that is very soothing to irritated or inflamed tissues. On the skin, it can be used for abscesses, boils, ulcers and varicose veins. Taken internally, it heals inflammation in the digestive system, from mouth and stomach ulcers to enteritis and colitis. *Althaea* root is particularly useful for these conditions. As soft as marshmallow describes its action as well as its texture.

The leaf, on the other hand, is more often used to treat respiratory problems, such as bronchitis and sore throats — it makes a wonderful, sweet-tasting cough syrup — and irritable conditions of the urinary tract, like cystitis and urethritis. It is very gentle and not unpleasant to taste, making it a useful remedy for children.

## Culinary

The roots of *Althaea* are sweetish and spongy, and in past times they have been used as a vegetable.

**FAMILY:**
Malvaceae

**COMMON ENGLISH NAMES:**
Marshmallow

**ORIGIN:**
Europe

**MAIN USES:**
Medicinal

**PARTS USED:**
Root and leaf

Nowadays marshmallows are sweets,
often toasted or floated in hot
chocolate, with a very faint
resemblance to the original
marshmallow roots.

## Cultivation

*Althaea officinalis* grows in
marshy and damp places, and
can be cultivated in a garden as long as
there is enough moisture. Many of
the Malvaceae family, such as
hollyhocks, hibiscus and tree mallow,
are common garden flowers.
Collect leaves in summer after
flowering, and dig the root in
late autumn.

# ANETHUM GRAVEOLENS

*A*nethum is one of the many useful carminative herbs that soothe intestinal spasm and promote good digestion. It helps to dispel wind, and its gentle action makes it one of the first choices for colic in babies and stomach upsets in general. *Anethum* combines well with *Matricaria*, *Althaea* and *Glycyrrhiza*, to name a few. Traditionally, it has been used on its own as dill water, or water containing essential oil of dill. As a home remedy, a tea made by steeping the seeds in hot water will work just as well.

## Culinary
The leaf, known as dill weed, is used for cooking. Its gentle piquancy makes it a useful companion to milder-tasting foods such as fish, often as an ingredient in a soup or sauce. It can also be added to salads and salad dressings, and is one of the spices used in pickling.

## Cultivation
*Anethum* is a hardy annual and easy to grow. To get top-quality seeds, wait until they are fully ripe before collecting them, and then dry them carefully, away from artificial heat or strong sunlight, to preserve the essential oils in them.

**FAMILY:**
*Umbelliferae*

**COMMON ENGLISH NAMES:**
*Dill*

**ORIGIN:**
*Mediterranean and Southern Russia*

**MAIN USES:**
*Medicinal, culinary*

**PARTS USED:**
*Seeds medicinally, leaves in cookery*

# ANGELICA ARCHANGELICA

Like many of the Umbelliferae, *Angelica* is a good digestive. Its slightly bitter flavour, combined with aromatic oils, makes it an appetite stimulant. It can be used to help recovery from anorexia nervosa, and from debilitating illnesses in general. It combines well with *Matricaria*, *Taraxacum* or *Verbena*. A robust, friendly herb, it is a good staff to lean on when you need support.

*Angelica* is also an expectorant, which means that it stimulates the flow of mucus in the respiratory tract. Together with the anti-inflammatory and anti-infective actions of the oils that it contains, this makes *Angelica* a powerful remedy for complaints such as chest infections, pleurisy and even pneumonia. Whenever the body needs assistance in making a cough more productive and driving out an infection, *Angelica* can help. Use it with herbs like

**FAMILY:**
*Umbelliferae*

**COMMON ENGLISH NAMES:**
*Angelica*

**ORIGIN:**
*Near East and Europe*

**MAIN USES:**
*Culinary*

**PARTS USED:**
*Roots and leaves medicinally, seeds and stems in cookery.*

*Glycyrrhiza, Inula, Thymus* or *Verbascum*.

## Culinary

*Angelica* stems are sold in crystallised form, often mixed with dried fruit, as flavouring for cakes. However, *Angelica* is much more versatile than that. The young stems can be added to rhubarb to improve its taste and digestibility. The stems can also be chewed raw; in Scandinavia they are considered a delicacy. The leaves are quite bitter, but if blanched they make a palatable vegetable, boiled or steamed like spinach.

The seeds are an ingredient of liqueurs such as vermouth and Chartreuse, and they could be added to brandy or gin to make an interesting *digestif*.

## Cultivation

*Angelica* likes damp soil, especially near water, and is thrives in shady positions. Dig the root in the autumn of its first year. Collect leaves and stems in June, and the seeds when ripe and dry at the end of the growing season.

# ANTHEMIS NOBILIS

*A*nthemis and its cousin, *Matricaria recutita* (German chamomile), are among the best-known healing herbs, and they both have a host of traditional uses. *Anthemis* is the more aromatic of the two: chamomile oil is distilled from its flowers, and is much used by aromatherapists for its calming and relaxing effects.

Prepared as a tea or a tincture, *Anthemis* soothes spasm and inflammation, eases pain and is gently sedative. This combination of actions makes it an ideal remedy for almost any childhood complaint, from colic to wakeful nights, and it will support whatever other herbs are used with it. *Anthemis* is also useful to adults suffering from insomnia, anxiety or any kind of nervous problem. On the physical side, it is calming and healing to an upset or inflamed digestive system, and can help sore throats and gingivitis. Used as a wash, it will help heal sore eyes, and skin problems like eczema and sunburn.

FAMILY:
*Compositae*

COMMON ENGLISH NAMES:
*Roman chamomile*

ORIGIN:
*Europe, North Africa and temperate Asia*

MAIN USES:
*Culinary, perfume*

PARTS USED:
*Flowers and herb*

## Culinary

Chamomile tea is now so popular that it is drunk simply as a pleasant and relaxing beverage, rather than being taken as a medicine. Thus it crosses the divide between herbs as foods and herbs as healing agents.

*Anthemis* is used to flavour manzanilla sherry, and is an ingredient in some beer recipes.

## Other

*Anthemis* was one of the traditional strewing herbs of the Middle Ages, spread indoors to give off its fresh scent when trodden on, and to mask less pleasant smells. The oil is used nowadays in the making of perfumes. A hair rinse containing *Anthemis* helps to lighten hair. Finally, it is well known as the 'plants' physician' in organic gardening. Grown near sickly plants, *Anthemis* seems to help them recover and to maintain good health.

## Caution

Not everyone likes the smell and taste of *Anthemis*, so it is worth checking before offering it. Herb teas should be a pleasure rather than a penance.

## Cultivation

This is the chamomile used for chamomile lawns, where the plants are grown so close together that they form a kind of mat, which gives off the distinctive chamomile scent when walked on. For a lawn, the plants should be kept low so that they do not flower. For medicinal use, the flowers are gathered when in bloom, between May and August.

# ANTHRISCUS CEREFOLIUM

*A*nthriscus, like many of the Umbelliferae, aids digestion by promoting the flow of digestive juices, easing spasm and helping to dispel wind. It is not one of the stronger healing herbs, so is better known in the kitchen than in the pharmacy.

*Anthriscus* was one of the traditional Lenten herbs eaten during the time of fasting before Easter, when it was thought to help cleanse the blood after the long winter. There is sound sense behind this: herbs do act as a tonic, especially when, as in Lent, they were the first fresh, green foods to be eaten after months of preserved foods and stored root vegetables. Most of the green garden vegetables are not ready to gather until late spring, so before the days of fast long-distance transport, these herbs played a vital part in enabling people to live well in the more northern parts of the world.

## Culinary

*Anthriscus* is a mild herb, often compared to *Petroselinum crispum* (parsley), although its taste is more delicate. It is one of the French *fines herbes*. The leaves can be added to salads, soups and sauces, and they go particularly well with eggs, chicken and white fish.

## Cultivation

*Anthriscus* is a cheerful biennial, easily grown from seed outdoors or in pots. Seed can be sown at intervals to keep a supply of fresh leaves available throughout the summer and autumn.

**FAMILY:**
*Umbelliferae*

**COMMON ENGLISH NAMES:**
*Chervil*

**ORIGIN:**
*Europe*

**MAIN USES:**
*Culinary*

**PARTS USED:**
*Leaves*

# APIUM GRAVEOLENS

The main use of *Apium* is in the treatment of rheumatism, arthritis and gout. It is diuretic, anti-inflammatory and helps to rid the body of excess uric acid, which can contribute to some of the adverse symptoms of these conditions. It can be combined with *Harpagophytum*, *Glycyrrhiza*, *Symphytum* and *Taraxacum*, for example.

*Apium* is also a urinary antiseptic, and can be used to treat cystitis, urethritis and kidney infections, together with such herbs as *Althaea*, *Zea*, *Agropyron* and *Arctostaphylos*.

## Culinary

Celery stalks, eaten raw as a salad vegetable or lightly cooked with many dishes, are too well known to need much description. The seeds are used as a spice in small quantities, adding a warm pungency to soups, stews and garnishes. Celeriac, a variation of celery, is grown for its root, which is very popular grated as a salad in France.

## Cultivation

As a vegetable, celery is quite a demanding plant, needing a rich, well-cultivated soil. The stems are earthed up as they grow, to blanch them and make them grow longer, producing the yellowish, delicately flavoured stalks that we value. For medicinal use it is the seeds that are required, so the plant is allowed to grow naturally and the seeds are harvested when ripe in the autumn.

**FAMILY:**
*Umbelliferae*

**COMMON ENGLISH NAMES:**
*Celery*

**ORIGIN:**
*Southern Europe; now widely cultivated*

**MAIN USES:**
*Culinary*

**PARTS USED:**
*Seed medicinally; stems, young leaves, seeds and roots in cookery*

# ARCTOSTAPHYLOS UVA-URSI

*A*rctostaphylos is a powerful urinary antiseptic, effective against infections of the kidney, bladder and urethra. It not only kills infective organisms, but also soothes inflammation and tones and strengthens the tissues in these areas. This makes it very useful for those who have suffered repeated infections and have used antibiotics, for while antibiotic drugs will kill micro-organisms, they leave the tissues in a weakened and congested state, vulnerable to further infection. *Arctostaphylos* works well with *Agropyron*, *Zea* and *Achillea*. Its effects are enhanced if the patient also drinks cranberry juice or lemon barley water, which are useful ways of making the urine more alkaline.

*Arctostaphylos* also has a part to play in restoring health when there are more chronic kidney problems, especially where there is a tendency to form gravel or stones.

| | |
|---:|---|
| **FAMILY:** | |
| *Ericaceae* | |

| | |
|---:|---|
| **COMMON ENGLISH NAMES:** | |
| *Bearberry* | |

| | |
|---:|---|
| **ORIGIN:** | |
| *Northern hemisphere, from the arctic to temperate zones, down to the Mediterranean* | |

| | |
|---:|---|
| **MAIN USES:** | |
| *Medicinal* | |

| | |
|---:|---|
| **PARTS USED:** | |
| *Leaves* | |

## Other

The leaves are so rich in tannins that they have been used to tan leather in the past.

## Caution

Not to be used in pregnancy.

## Cultivation

*Arctostaphylos* is not usually cultivated, although it would make an attractive ground cover in damp and shady places. Dense clusters of flowers bloom in May and June before the dark green, glossy leaves appear. The berries, which are bright red, ripen in autumn, and are much loved by bears — hence its common name.

# ARTEMISIA ABSINTHIUM

T he artemisias are ancient healing herbs. According to legend, they were discovered by the goddess Artemis, for whom they are named. She then gave them to the centaur Chiron as medicines for humankind. The intense bitterness of *Artemisia absinthium* is legendary. Used in small quantities, it will re-invigorate a sluggish digestive system, and it is a traditional way to deter, or eliminate, parasites of all descriptions, especially roundworm and pinworm. It also changes secretions, making the user less of a target for mosquitoes and other biting insects. As a result, it is useful herb for

**FAMILY:**
*Compositae*

**COMMON ENGLISH NAMES:**
*Wormwood*

**ORIGIN:**
*Europe and Siberia; naturalised in USA*

**MAIN USES:**
*Medicinal*

**PARTS USED:**
*Leaves and flowers*

travellers, who are more vulnerable to unfamiliar infections.

The essential oil has a directly stimulating effect on the central nervous system and can be used, with care, in the treatment of depression, or for people who need to remain alert under stress, such as hard-pressed students.

## Culinary

Wormwood is far too bitter to find a place in cookery, but it does have one very famous use: it is the key ingredient in absinthe. This ruinously potent liqueur used to be highly valued by poets and other creative artists because of its stimulating effect on the brain. Indeed, in small doses, *Artemisia absinthium* will wake up and clear a fogged mind, but used too often or in too large a dose, it can produce giddiness and even seizures.

## Caution

Wormwood is not recommended for self-medication; consult a professional herbalist about its use. It should not to be used in pregnancy, when breastfeeding or for young children.

## Cultivation

Many artemisias are grown as garden plants, and they do well in a relatively dry, not too sunny situation. They can be spread by dividing the roots in autumn, by cuttings, or by sowing seed. Gather leaves and flowers from July to September.

# ARTEMISIA DRACUNCULUS

This is the mildest of the artemisias. It is a gentle digestive, but used more in cookery than in medicine.

## Culinary

There are two kinds of tarragon used in the kitchen: French tarragon, which has a better flavour, and Russian (*Artemisia dracunculoides*), also known as false tarragon. In this herb, the bitterness of the artemisias is mellowed to a warm pungency, and so it makes a useful companion to the cooler tastes — in salads, for example, and mild-tasting vegetables like artichokes and courgettes. It is probably best known in tarragon vinegar.

## Cultivation

Divide the roots in spring, and grow in a warm, dry situation. Tarragon does not like frost, but does well as a pot plant. Pick the leaves in autumn.

FAMILY:
*Compositae*

COMMON ENGLISH NAMES:
*French tarragon*

ORIGIN:
*Southern Europe, Siberia*

MAIN USES:
*Medicinal, culinary*

PARTS USED:
*Leaves*

# ARTEMISIA VULGARE

*A*rtemisia vulgare is a valuable digestive tonic; its bitterness stimulates the appetite and helps in the breakdown of fats. This makes it very useful for those who have gall-bladder problems, or who have had their gall bladders removed. It combines well with *Taraxacum radix*, *Rumex crispus* and *Glycyrrhiza glabra*, for example.

This herb has similar stimulating properties to those of *Artemisia absinthium*. It can help in the treatment of depression and low spirits, when used with herbs like *Hypericum*, *Avena* or *Verbena*.

In traditional Chinese medicine, the leaves are used to make moxa, which is burned near the skin to raise vital energy in that area. This is beneficial for many rheumatic and muscular conditions.

**FAMILY:**
*Compositae*

**COMMON ENGLISH NAMES:**
*Mugwort*

**ORIGIN:**
*Northern Europe*

**MAIN USES:**
*Medicinal*

**PARTS USED:**
*Leaves, root*

## Culinary

Mugwort used to be used as a bitter flavouring for beer, but has been superseded by hops (*Humulus lupulus*). Its taste is too strong for culinary use.

## Other

An interesting use of *Artemisia vulgare* – which fits in with its ability to raise mental energy and clarify the mind – is to encourage lucid dreams. If you sleep with a sprig of mugwort under your pillow, you are more likely to have lucid dreams, those in which you know, or become aware, that you are dreaming. I cannot vouch personally for this, but if you are interested in dream exploration, it is worth a try.

## Caution

Like *Artemisia absinthium*, this herb was traditionally used to get rid of worms and other parasites, but do not use it in this way without professional guidance. The dosage needed to expel worms may be quite high, and can lead to purging, which can be very unpleasant. Although milder than *Artemisia absinthium*, mugwort is not suitable for pregnant and breastfeeding women or young children.

## Cultivation

*Artemisia vulgare* grows wild in Europe, and will grow anywhere in a warm, dry situation.

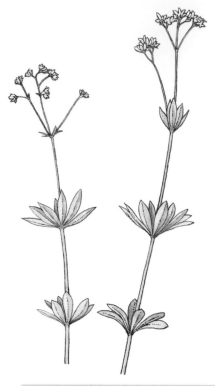

# ASPERULA ODORATA

*A*sperula used to be used in the Middle Ages for healing wounds and helping digestion, but fell out of fashion, although its cousin, *Galium aparine* (goosegrass), is very popular with modern herbalists. *Asperula* is still highly thought of in France, where it is used as a tranquillising tea to soothe and calm the nerves. It also encourages restful sleep, without any of the undesirable side effects of sleeping pills.

## Culinary
In Germany, the herb is called *Waldemeister* (master of the wood), and it is steeped in white wine to make the Maibowle, which is drunk on the first of May.

## Other
*Asperula*'s main claim to fame nowadays is its perfume. When dried, it gives off a fresh, sweet smell, like newly mown hay, which can last for many years. The herb was used for strewing and for stuffing mattresses, but today it is used in perfumery, and finds its way into pot-pourris and pomanders. It can be used like lavender to keep linen fresh and to deter insects.

## Cultivation
*Asperula* is a common wildflower of woods and shady places. It is easy to grow, and will naturalise readily under trees or hedges, where its tiny, white, star-like flowers will appear in May and June.

FAMILY:
*Rubiaceae*

COMMON ENGLISH NAMES:
*Sweet woodruff*

ORIGIN:
*Northern and Central Europe*

MAIN USES:
*Medicinal, perfume*

PARTS USED:
*Herb*

# AVENA SATIVA

*A*vena is a very good example of the way that herbs bridge the divide between food and medicine. It is nutritious and easily digested, useful after illness or wherever someone needs building up. It also supports and strengthens the nervous system. For anyone who is run down, exhausted or suffering from the effects of stress, *Avena* is a true friend in need. It helps to lift depression and put new heart into tired people. Considering that so many ailments arise when we are depleted of energy or over-extended, it is not surprising that *Avena* is one of the mainstays of modern herbal medicine. It works well together with *Verbena* and *Scutellaria*, among many others.

Used on the skin, an *Avena* poultice is soothing and healing for any form of inflammation. For acute eczema, handfuls of oatmeal may be added to a warm bath. This makes it a very useful first-aid treatment for a child in acute distress.

| FAMILY: |
| --- |
| *Graminaceae* |

| COMMON ENGLISH NAMES: |
| --- |
| *Oats* |

| ORIGIN: |
| --- |
| *Widespread in cultivation* |

| MAIN USES: |
| --- |
| *Medicinal, culinary* |

| PARTS USED: |
| --- |
| *Seeds and straw* |

## Culinary

*Avena*, in the form of rolled oats or oatmeal, is familiar as porridge or gruel, which has long been seen as a very suitable food for invalids and children, and a useful sustaining breakfast in the northern climates where oats are grown. *Avena* is also used in baking, alone or mixed with other grains. So what your grandmother told you is true – porridge really is good for you.

## Cultivation

*Avena* is grown as a field crop for animal and human food, and harvested in August when the seed is ripe.

# BERBERIS AQUIFOLIUM

*B*erberis aquifolium and *Berberis vulgaris* have some
constituents in common with *Hydrastis canadensis*
(golden seal). Because *Hydrastis* has become so rare, they
are often preferred by modern herbalists. Both these, and
other members of the berberis family, are tonic to the
liver and gall bladder, waking up the digestion and
improving assimilation of food. They are good, safe
laxatives, often useful in chronic constipation, where
continued use will slowly but surely persuade the bowel
to move more easily and regularly.

    *Berberis aquifolium* has a particular reputation for
helping clear up chronic scaly skin conditions,
especially eczema and psoriasis. This must be partly
due to its cleansing action on the liver, but since it
is more use in this respect than *Berberis vulgaris*, other
qualities must also come into play. It works well
with skin tonics such as *Urtica*, *Rumex crispus* and
*Trifolium pratense*.

## Caution
Not to be used in pregnancy.

## Cultivation
*Berberis aquifolium* is a
common garden shrub
that is now grown in
many countries. It is
hardy and not too
demanding to grow.
Collect rhizomes and
roots in the autumn.

**FAMILY:**
*Berberidaceae*

**COMMON ENGLISH NAMES:**
*Oregon grape, mountain grape,
mahonia*

**ORIGIN:**
*Western USA*

**MAIN USES:**
*Medicinal*

**PARTS USED:**
*Rhizome and root*

# BERBERIS VULGARIS

*B*erberis vulgaris is one of our best liver tonics, helping convalescence from hepatitis and other liver complaints, and aiding recovery after heavy drug use. Jaundice, which is a sign that the liver is under stress rather than a disease in itself, used to be seen as a clear call for the healing action of *Berberis vulgaris*.

It promotes the flow of bile, so helping the digestion of fats and acting as a gentle laxative. If there is inflammation of the gall bladder, whether there are stones present or not, *B. vulgaris* will help to soothe the inflammation and improve its working. For those who have had the gall bladder removed, herbs like *B. vulgaris* will keep the digestion working smoothly. It combines well with *Verbena*,

**FAMILY:**
*Berberidaceae*

**COMMON ENGLISH NAMES:**
*Barberry*

**ORIGIN:**
*North Africa, temperate Asia*

**MAIN USES:**
*Medicinal*

**PARTS USED:**
*Bark and root bark*

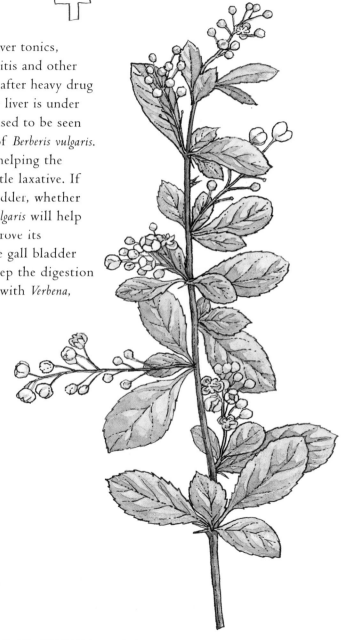

*Taraxacum radix* and *Fumaria*, as well as carminatives such as *Carum carvi* and *Mentha piperita*.

   *B. vulgaris* is a useful anti-malarial, and is active against Leishmania infections, so it's a good herb to take as a prophylactic if you expect to be exposed to these infections.

## Culinary

The berries are astringent but refreshing, and a good source of vitamin C. In the past they were used to make pickles and jellies.

## Other

The roots and stem-bark can be used to make a yellow dye, which traditionally has been used on wool, leather and linen.

## Caution

Not to be used in pregnancy.

## Cultivation

*B. vulgaris* is a common garden shrub, grown for its yellow flowers, which bloom in May and June, and red berries. Its main drawback is wicked thorns, which easily break off in your hands. There is a belief in Italy that it was one of the plants used in Christ's crown of thorns. Grow *B. vulgaris* from seeds or cuttings in spring or autumn, or from suckers. Collect bark in spring or autumn.

# BETULA ALBA AND SPECIES

*B*etula contains a high proportion of salicylic acid and this makes it a useful remedy for the inflammatory problems caused by arthritis, both rheumatic and osteoarthritis, and for the pain of gout. It can be taken internally, applied as a poultice or massaged into affected joints in an oil base. Muscular pains are also helped in this way. *Betula* combines well with *Glycyrrhiza* or *Harpagophytum* for these problems. Like *Salix*, which is also rich in salicylic acid, its slender, flexible form impressed our ancestors — sympathetic magic that is solidly rooted in reality. Use it for suppleness of mind as well as body.

   *Betula* is also a urinary antiseptic and diuretic, so it can be used to treat urinary infections, alongside herbs such as *Arctostaphylos* and *Agropyron*.

FAMILY:

*Betulaceae*

COMMON ENGLISH NAMES:

*White birch*

ORIGIN:

*Europe and Northern Asia*

MAIN USES:

*Medicinal*

PARTS USED:

*Leaves and bark*

## Culinary

Birch wine can be made from the sap that flows from the tree when the trunk is cut. This is collected in spring, like maple syrup, and fermented with yeast, honey, lemon and cloves.

## Other

*Betula* bark was once used in making a form of paper. The wood is used variously, while the tannins and distilled oil are used in processing leather.

## Cultivation

*Betula* grows wild in its native habitat, particularly on heaths and uplands. Many varieties are grown in gardens for the beauty of the bark, which comes in many colours from pure white to deep red.

# BORAGO OFFICINALIS

*Borago* is a tough and friendly herb, with a longstanding reputation for dispelling melancholy, lifting depression and helping people to cope with 'difficult' situations. Up-to-date research shows that it supports and restores the action of the adrenal glands, which help us to deal with stresses of all sorts – physical, emotional or psychological. This makes *Borago* suitable for those who have had to use steroid drugs for various medical conditions, since these tend to depress the adrenal glands. For anyone who is depressed, run down, suffering from post-viral fatigue or ME, *Borago* is worth a try. Use it with *Hypericum*, *Scutellaria*, *Verbena* or *Avena*.

*Borago* has found a new use in recent times. Its seeds are a rich source of oil containing gamma-linolenic acid, or GLA, which is also found in evening primrose seed (*Oenothera biennis*). Remarketed as starflower oil, this has potent anti-inflammatory and tonic effects. It is particularly useful in the treatment of eczema, arthritis, menstruation problems and adverse symptoms of the menopause.

**FAMILY:**
*Boraginaceae*

**COMMON ENGLISH NAMES:**
*Borage, starflower*

**ORIGIN:**
*Europe and Near East*

**MAIN USES:**
*Medicinal*

**PARTS USED:**
*Aerial parts, seeds*

It also helps to stave off the symptoms of multiple sclerosis.

## Culinary

The young leaves can be used in salads. Although they have quite a rough texture, the flavour is cool and fresh, like cucumber. The flowers are more popular, and they are pretty too; they can also be added to summer punches and fruit cups, or candied.

## Cultivation

*Borago* is an annual, easily grown from seed. It re-seeds itself and spreads happily. Collect the leaves just before the flowers come out, the flowers in first bloom, and the seeds when they are ripe.

# BRASSICA ALBA/NIGRA

The best-known use of *Brassica* is probably as a poultice, applied to the skin wherever there is pain in the muscles or joints. A mustard bath has a similar, though less concentrated, effect. *Brassica* is mildly irritating to the skin, bringing a flush of blood to the area, which has the effect of stimulating the circulation, helping to dispel the products of inflammation, and so relieving pain and spasm. It can be combined with a soothing herb like *Symphytum* or *Ulmus fulva*, or with other warming anti-inflammatory agents like *Juniperus communis* or *Lavandula officinalis*.

To make a poultice, mix 100 grams of freshly ground seed with warm water to form a thick paste,

FAMILY:
*Cruciferae*

COMMON ENGLISH NAMES:
*White or black mustard*

ORIGIN:
*Europe and Asia*

MAIN USES:
*Culinary*

PARTS USED:
*Seeds*

and spread it on a piece of cloth. Put gauze over the affected area to stop the poultice from sticking, and lay the poultice on top. Leave it on for about a minute.

For a mustard bath, bruise a tablespoonful of seeds and pour on a litre of boiling water. Infuse for five minutes, strain and add the liquid to the bath.

Taken internally in a medicinal dose, *Brassica* brings on a sweat, helping the body to deal with fever, colds, influenza and bronchitis.

## Culinary

Young mustard leaves can be used in salads, like their close relative, rocket; older leaves are too pungent. It is the seeds that are most used, fried as a spice in Indian cookery, or ground and made into a condiment in Europe. Mustard brings heat to rich dishes, especially red meats, improving their digestibility and enhancing their taste. It is also a useful pickling spice, both for its flavour and for the preserving qualities of the mustard oil.

## Other

The mustards are also grown as a fodder crop for animals, and as a green manure.

## Cultivation

The mustards are widely grown commercially. They do best in dry weather. Collect seeds in late summer.

# CALENDULA OFFICINALIS

*C*alendula has the place of honour in a herbal first-aid kit. It is anti-infective, anti-inflammatory, and its astringency helps to seal and protect wounds. Used as an infusion or made into a cream, it helps with any skin inflammation, cuts, bruises, burns, scalds and insect bites. If you want to make a cream, use only the petals so as to get the beautiful deep golden colour. It also plays a valuable role in the management of chronic or slow-healing skin conditions, such as varicose veins and ulcers, eczema and acne.

Taken internally, *Calendula* helps to heal mouth and stomach ulcers and sore throats, as well as easing indigestion. It works well with *Althaea*, *Symphytum*, *Filipendula* and *Glycyrrhiza*, among others.

*Calendula* is the first herb of choice whenever there is a

**FAMILY:**

*Compositae*

**COMMON ENGLISH NAMES:**

*Marigold*

**ORIGIN:**

*Southern Europe; now widespread in cultivation*

**MAIN USES:**

*Medicinal*

**PARTS USED:**

*Flower heads, especially the petals*

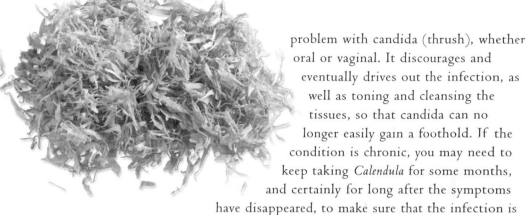

problem with candida (thrush), whether oral or vaginal. It discourages and eventually drives out the infection, as well as toning and cleansing the tissues, so that candida can no longer easily gain a foothold. If the condition is chronic, you may need to keep taking *Calendula* for some months, and certainly for long after the symptoms have disappeared, to make sure that the infection is completely eradicated. Use it with *Thymus*, *Commiphora molmol* (myrrh) or *Melaleuca* (ti-tree) oil (for external use only) to enhance the effects.

If it becomes necessary to take antibiotics for any kind of infection, taking *Calendula* at the same time will help to ensure that candida does not appear after the antibiotics are finished.

## Culinary
The petals were once used to colour cheese and butter yellow.

## Cultivation
*Calendula* is a very common garden flower. Sow seed in April. It will then re-seed every year. Just looking at the clear orange flowers is said to be enough to lighten the spirits.

# CAPSICUM MINIMUM

## FAMILY:
Solanaceae

## COMMON ENGLISH NAMES:
Cayenne, chilli pepper

## ORIGIN:
Zanzibar; now widely cultivated in tropical and subtropical climates

## MAIN USES:
Medicinal, culinary

## PARTS USED:
Fruit

Like most other culinary spices, *Capsicum* is an aid to digestion, but in medicinal terms it is more valued for its effects on the circulatory system. It is a potent peripheral vasodilator, stimulating blood supply to the smaller blood vessels that carry blood to the skin and the extremities of the body. For anyone who suffers from cold hands and feet, whether it is just a mild inconvenience or the torment of chilblains or Raynaud's disease, *Capsicum* will help. It will also ease the aches and pains of rheumatism, and speed the healing of muscular sprains and strains.

When applied to the skin, *Capsicum* will bring blood to the area, thus easing local pain and inflammation. A useful ointment for chilblains can be made by melting 50g vaseline in a water bath, and adding half a teaspoonful of *Capsicum* powder.

## Culinary

*Capsicum* is the hottest of all spices, its flavour almost completely obscured by its fire. It is usually combined with other spices and seasonings to produce a more balanced taste, and is found in most of the world's traditions of cookery.

## Caution

The required dose of *Capsicum* is very small. Whereas most herbs can be taken in tincture form by the teaspoonful, a drop of *Capsicum* mixed with water or other tinctures is enough. If applied to the skin and left on for too long or used in too great a concentration, it can cause blisters.

## Cultivation

*Capsicum* needs a long growing season, plenty of hot sun, and steady watering. Outside the tropics, it can be grown in a greenhouse or on a windowsill. Harvest the ripe fruits when they are dark red, and then dry them.

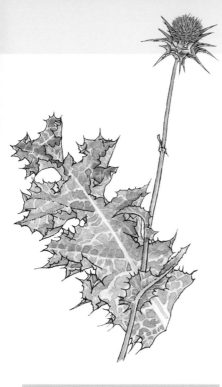

# CARDUUS MARIANUS

*C*arduus is one of the bitter herbs that act as liver tonics, promoting the flow of bile and so helping with gall-bladder problems. It also helps stimulate the flow of breast milk, and is a safe herb for nursing mothers.

Research has shown that not only does *Carduus* help the liver to recover from illness or poisoning, but it can also help protect it from damage if taken prophylactically. People who have taken *Carduus* before an alcohol binge show less liver damage afterwards than those who have not, and they recover faster. *Carduus* is therefore a very valuable herb for those who have ingested toxins of any sort – and for those who are intending to. This is not, of course, a free ticket to substance abuse; the obvious use is for people who have to take a lot of orthodox drugs. For example, it will aid recovery

**ALSO KNOWN AS:**
*Silybum marianum*

**FAMILY:**
*Compositae*

**COMMON ENGLISH NAMES:**
Milk thistle

**ORIGIN:**
Europe and Asia; now widespread

**MAIN USES:**
Medicinal

**PARTS USED:**
Seeds

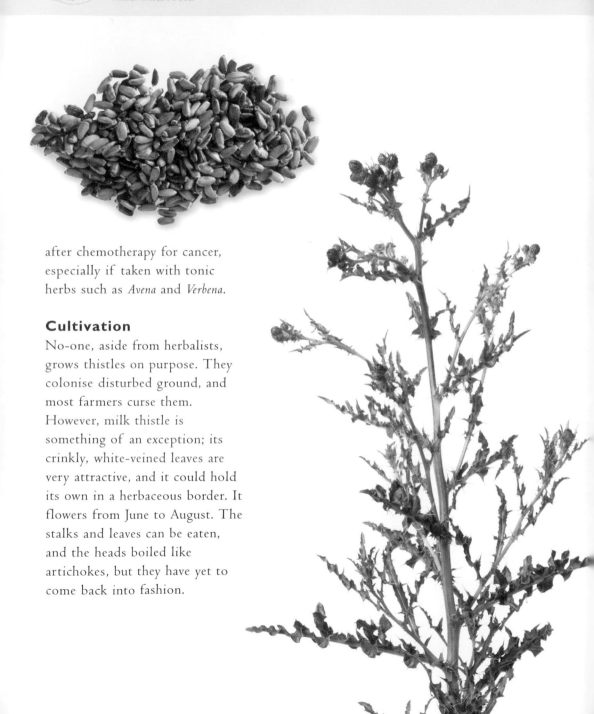

after chemotherapy for cancer, especially if taken with tonic herbs such as *Avena* and *Verbena*.

## Cultivation

No-one, aside from herbalists, grows thistles on purpose. They colonise disturbed ground, and most farmers curse them. However, milk thistle is something of an exception; its crinkly, white-veined leaves are very attractive, and it could hold its own in a herbaceous border. It flowers from June to August. The stalks and leaves can be eaten, and the heads boiled like artichokes, but they have yet to come back into fashion.

# CARUM CARVI

*C*arum is another of the carminatives, herbs that improve digestion, ease colic and wind, and stimulate the appetite. It is a useful remedy for childhood colic, and its mild astringency helps to calm loose bowels. It combines well with *Matricaria*, *Melissa* and *Agrimonia*, for example.

Traditionally, *Carum* is used to promote the flow of breast milk, and to stimulate the flow of mucus in bronchitis and bronchitic asthma.

## Culinary

Caraway is an old favourite in Europe and Asia, both in sweet and savoury cookery. Its warm, piquant, slightly astringent taste seems to enhance all sorts of dishes. It can be baked in cakes and pastries or with fruit as a sweet dish, or added to soup, cheese, cabbage or bread as a savoury. It is an essential ingredient of Hungarian goulash, or beef stew.

*Carum* also finds its way into many liqueurs and cordials.

## Cultivation

A biennial herb or spice, *Carum* is grown outdoors in warm and sunny climates, or indoors in the north. Collect the fruit in August. If it thrives, it will self-seed for future years.

**FAMILY:**
*Umbelliferae*

**COMMON ENGLISH NAMES:**
*Caraway*

**ORIGIN:**
*Northern and Central Europe and Asia*

**MAIN USES:**
*Medicinal, culinary*

**PARTS USED:**
*Fruit (usually called seed)*

# CASSIA ANGUSTIFOLIA AND CASSIA SENNA

The sole use of *Cassia* is to relieve constipation, which it does very effectively. It is a powerful cathartic, but will cause griping if used alone; combine it with carminatives like *Elettaria, Cardamomum* or *Zingiber* to improve the taste as well as the action.

*Cassia* is in many over-the-counter remedies for constipation, and a lot of people end up taking it on a regular basis, without even considering that they are taking strong medication. While it relieves the symptoms, it does not go any way towards helping the causes of constipation. It should, therefore, only be used as first aid, for example, after an operation, when the bowels may be reluctant to move. It is habit-forming, in that it works by irritating the bowels into action, and they soon become dependent upon this stimulus.

Constipation can be a symptom of many things. First, try to increase your consumption of fresh fruit and vegetables, and take some moderate to vigorous exercise every day. Next, try bitter herbs like *Taraxacum radix* or *Rumex*. The next step, rather than resorting to purgatives like *Cassia*, is to consult a professional herbalist or a doctor.

| FAMILY: |
| --- |
| *Leguminosae* |

| COMMON ENGLISH NAMES: |
| --- |
| *Senna* |

| ORIGIN: |
| --- |
| *Egypt, Sudan, Jordan and India* |

| MAIN USES: |
| --- |
| *Medicinal* |

| PARTS USED: |
| --- |
| *Fruit pods* |

## Caution

The use of any strong purgatives is not advisable in pregnancy or while breastfeeding, and *Cassia* is no exception to this rule.

## Cultivation

Grown commercially in its native habitats. The fruit pods are dried before use.

# CINNAMOMUM ZEYLANICUM

In addition to its digestive action, *Cinnamomum* is a circulatory stimulant, and it can be used with other herbs to 'warm up' the prescription. It can help with nausea and vomiting, and may be useful in pregnancy sickness. Its astringency, combined with its aromatic properties, makes it useful in the treatment of irritable bowel and colitis. Mix it with herbs such as *Symphytum*, *Matricaria* and *Melissa*.

Essential oil of cinnamon is popular with aromatherapists. It must be diluted with a neutral oil base, or it can be mixed into a cream; if it is too strong it can cause irritation. Applied to the skin, it warms the immediate area, and is useful for aches and pains, especially with other oils such as *Juniperus*, *Rosmarinus* and *Myrtus communis*.

**FAMILY:**

*Lauraceae*

**COMMON ENGLISH NAMES:**

*Cinnamon*

**ORIGIN:**

*Sri Lanka; now widely cultivated in the tropics*

**MAIN USES:**

*Medicinal, culinary*

**PARTS USED:**

*Dried inner bark of the shoots*

## Culinary

*Cinnamomum* is very aromatic, with a sweetish taste. In the north it has been mainly used as a sweet spice, in baking, with fruit, and to flavour drinks, especially winter punch. A favourite cold remedy is a drink of lemon juice in hot water with cinnamon and honey. In other parts of the world, especially in Indian cooking, it is often one of a mixture of spices in savoury dishes.

## Cultivation

*Cinnamomum* grows in sand, and needs shelter, an even temperature and constant rain. The trees reach 6–9 metres in height.

# CITRUS SPP.

In traditional Chinese medicine, mandarin orange peel (*Citrus reticulata*) is used, mixed with other herbs, as an energy regulator. In the West, *Citrus* is best known in essential oils. They are all antiseptic and anti-inflammatory, useful for skin problems from acne and greasy skin to corns and chilblains.

Lemon juice helps to cleanse and stimulate the liver, and traditionally it has been used, mixed with olive oil, to try to dissolve gallstones. While it certainly helps in the treatment of gall-bladder problems, I have never come across any solid evidence that this treatment actually works.

## Culinary

The citrus family has a multitude of uses in the kitchen. The peels are used to add zest to many dishes, the raw fruits and their juice can be eaten fresh, or cooked in many ways. Lemon and lime, in particular, are used in both sweet and savoury dishes. Orange flower water is an ingredient in biscuit making. The whole family is rich in vitamin C and bioflavonoids.

## Other

Citrus oils are used to make scents and perfumes. Flower waters are also valued for their fragrance. They find their way into soaps, detergents, cosmetics and air fresheners.

## Caution

Some oils, notably lemon and bergamot, can cause a phototoxic reaction in the skin if exposed to sunlight.

## Cultivation

The Citrus family does well in subtropical and Mediterranean climates.

| | |
|---|---|
| FAMILY: | *Rutaceae* |
| COMMON ENGLISH NAMES: | *Orange, lemon, lime, grapefruit, mandarin, neroli, bergamot* |
| ORIGIN: | *India, China; cultivated elsewhere* |
| MAIN USES: | *Culinary, perfume* |
| PARTS USED: | *Fruits, flowers, peel* |

# CORIANDRUM SATIVUM

*C*oriandrum used to have a place in the British pharmacopoeia for its ability to disguise the unpleasant tastes of other medications. It is also the herb of choice to accompany senna (*Cassia angustifolia*), both for the taste and for its antispasmodic action, where a strong laxative is needed.

Otherwise, *Coriandrum* is another useful carminative, easing wind and bloating, calming colic, and stimulating the appetite. Like *Foeniculum* (fennel) and *Anethum graveolens* (dill), it is very suitable for children; even small babies can be given an infusion to ease the pain of colic.

## Culinary

The leaves and the seeds of *Coriandrum* have two quite distinct smells and tastes. The leaves are almost foetid when fresh, though they become more fragrant in cooking, and the seeds are much sweeter. Both are used extensively in Eastern cuisines in various ways. In Britain, *Coriandrum* has been used to flavour gin and other liquors. English-grown *Coriandrum* is said to have the finest flavour.

## Cultivation

*Coriandrum* is an annual, easy to grow from seed. It will survive fairly well outdoors, even in northern climates, though the seed may not ripen. Harvest leaves when fresh and green, before flowering. Collect the flowering heads in late summer and leave them to ripen; then it is easy to shake out the seeds.

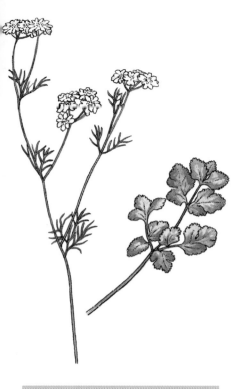

FAMILY:

*Umbelliferae*

COMMON ENGLISH NAMES:

*Coriander*

ORIGIN:

*Southern Europe*

MAIN USES:

*Medicinal, culinary*

PARTS USED:

*Seeds and leaves*

# CRATAEGUS OXYACANTHOIDES ✝

*C*srataegus is a heart helper; think of it for any situation where the heart is in need of support. It helps to normalise heart function, bringing it to maximum efficiency. Thus, it is useful where there is heart failure or weakness, irregular heartbeat or palpitations, although of course it cannot correct valve defects. It does, however, have a tonic effect on the walls of the blood vessels, so it is very valuable to those suffering from arteriosclerosis and the symptoms associated with it, such as angina and

**FAMILY:**
*Rosaceae*

**COMMON ENGLISH NAMES:**
*Hawthorn, may tree*

**ORIGIN:**
*Europe, North Africa and Western Asia*

**MAIN USES:**
*Medicinal*

**PARTS USED:**
*Leaves, flowers, berries*

intermittent claudication. Abnormal blood pressure, whether high or low, will respond well to *Crataegus*. It works well with companions like *Achillea*, *Tilia* and *Viscum*.

*Crataegus* will also benefit veins as well as arteries, helping with varicose veins, varicose eczema and phlebitis. Good combinations here might include *Calendula*, *Aesculus* and *Achillea*.

## Culinary

The young leaves can be eaten raw. The berries can be made into a liqueur with brandy, and conserves used to be made of them.

## Caution

As always with potentially serious conditions such as angina, heart failure and high blood pressure, it is wise to seek professional help. Herbs can be very effective, either alone or in combination with orthodox drugs, but expert advice is worth having.

## Cultivation

*Crataegus* is common in hedges and on hillsides throughout its habitat. The leaves are collected when young and fresh, the flowers when newly opened, and the berries in September and October, before the frosts.

# CUMINUM CYMINUM

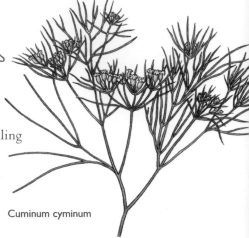

*Cuminum cyminum*

*Cuminum* is another of the many Umbelliferae that are useful digestive stimulants. They are all warm and benevolent, promoting appetite and dispelling wind and griping. Traditionally, herbalists found it to be stronger and more effective than *Foeniculum* and *Carum carvi*, but these have come to be more popular because of their more pleasant taste.

## Culinary

*Cuminum* is one of the curry spices in Indian and Middle Eastern cookery, often paired with *Coriandrum* (coriander), and it is popular in Mexico too. It was a favourite condiment of the Greeks and Romans, and was highly prized in Europe in the Middle Ages, but was later superseded by *Carum carvi* (caraway), whose flavour came to be preferred.

It is a useful herb to pair with cabbage and beans, and can be added to soups and stews. It has a warm, slightly bitter taste, and is offset well by other herbs and spices like *Coriandrum* (coriander), *Foeniculum* (fennel) or *Pimpinella anisum* (anise), which have a more piquant aroma.

| FAMILY: |
| --- |
| *Umbelliferae* |

| COMMON ENGLISH NAMES: |
| --- |
| *Cumin* |

| ORIGIN: |
| --- |
| *Upper Egypt; spread to Near East, India, China and Southern Europe* |

| MAIN USES: |
| --- |
| *Medicinal, culinary* |

| PARTS USED: |
| --- |
| *Seeds* |

## Cultivation

*Cuminum* is an annual, and not hard to grow, even in Northern Europe, as long as it is provided with a light soil, plenty of warmth and sunshine. The seeds, or more properly fruits, are threshed from the flower heads, which are harvested when they begin to die back.

Echinacea angustifolia

**FAMILY:**

*Compositae*

**COMMON ENGLISH NAMES:**

*Echinacea, coneflower*

**ORIGIN:**

*Western USA; now widely cultivated*

**MAIN USES:**

*Medicinal*

**PARTS USED:**

*Root and rhizome*

# ECHINACEA PALLIDA/ PURPUREA/ ANGUSTIFOLIA

*E*chinacea must be one of the best known, and certainly most used, herbs of our times, and you can buy preparations containing it from any ordinary chemist. It stimulates the immune system, helping the body to rid itself of infections of all sorts, not just bacterial but also viral, fungal and those caused by other micro-organisms. It can do this because, unlike antibiotic drugs, it does not work primarily by killing the infectious organisms (although this is part of what it does), but by waking up the body's defences and helping them to work more efficiently.

Thus, it can be used in two ways. In acute infections, relatively large doses of *Echinacea* can be used – up to 5ml tincture every two hours for an adult – together with other herbs, depending on the type of illness. For colds, flu and sore throats, use it with *Achillea* and *Sambucus*. For sinusitis, it works well with *Solidago* (golden rod). For chest

infections, use *Thymus*, *Inula* or *Angelica*. For urinary problems, combine it with *Arctostaphylos* and *Agropyron*. It can also be used as a lotion externally, for sores, cuts, infected acne and eczema.

The second way to use it is as a preventative. If you are prone to infections, have had to use antibiotics too many times, or have been advised to have flu vaccinations but are not happy with the idea, *Echinacea* can be taken safely and continually at a much lower dose. Even just a few drops a day will help to activate the immune system, and its effects do not diminish over time. It is particularly useful to take it in this way in autumn and in the spring, when the change in seasons makes people more vulnerable to infection.

## Cultivation

*Echinacea* is a tall plant with striking, purple, daisy-like flowers. Increasingly grown as a commercial field crop in temperate climates, it also finds a place in ornamental gardens. For medicinal use, the roots are dug up in the autumn.

# ELETTARIA CARDAMOMUM

Cardamomum is a useful digestive in its own right, but it has mainly been used to complement and flavour various medicinal preparations. It is found in laxative and tonic mixtures, where it helps to boost the appetite, improve digestion and regulate the bowels. I find it useful as an ingredient in prescriptions for irritable bowel, where its gentle anti-inflammatory action may be better tolerated than some of the more powerful herbs. It works well with *Matricaria*, *Melissa* and *Symphytum*.

## Culinary

*Cardamomum* is well known as a curry spice, but the seeds can also be chewed to sweeten the breath, ground and added to coffee, or used to flavour cakes and liqueurs. The taste is sweetish and intensely aromatic.

| FAMILY: |
| --- |
| *Zingiberaceae* |

| COMMON ENGLISH NAMES: |
| --- |
| *Cardamom* |

| ORIGIN: |
| --- |
| *Southern India* |

| MAIN USES: |
| --- |
| *Medicinal, culinary, perfume* |

| PARTS USED: |
| --- |
| *Seeds* |

## Other

The distilled oil is used in perfumery.

## Cultivation

*Cardamomum* is a forest plant, flowering in April and May. Harvesting is done in the dry season between October and December.

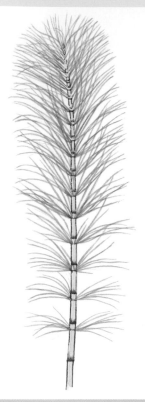

# EQUISETUM ARVENSE

*E*quisetum is a strange and ancient plant, a descendant of the giant horsetails of the Carboniferous era. It looks skeletal, and this is a clue to one of its virtues; it is a rich source of silicon, which makes it a healer of wounds when used externally, and a builder of bones if you take it as tea or tincture. It is a good friend to those recovering from injuries, or at risk of osteoporosis.

Its more traditional use is in the treatment of genito-urinary problems. It is a specific for prostate problems, whether to do with inflammation or benign enlargement, and for this it combines with *Smilax ornata* (sarsaparilla) or *Hydrangea arborescens* (hydrangea). It can also be very useful for bed-wetting and urinary incontinence in children, usually combined with nervous-system-supporting herbs such as *Matricaria* and *Tilia*.

## Culinary

The young shoots can be boiled or steamed and eaten with butter.

## Cultivation

*Equisetum* is a common wild plant of woods and damp places. A close cousin, *Equisetum arvense*, is a field weed that is very difficult to get rid of, but is also used in medicine. The stems are cut and dried in early summer.

# ERYTHRAEA CENTAURIUM

*E*rythraea is one of the bitter herbs, but it is gentle enough to be used for children, whenever an appetite stimulant is needed or there are stomach problems. It works well with *Matricaria*, *Melissa* or *Althaea* in this context. It is a useful herb in convalescence, especially when the liver is in need of restoring after illness or drug therapy.

For adults, too, it is a reliable tonic, and it can be given to those suffering from anorexia nervosa as well as to those who have more straightforward digestive troubles. For elderly folk who have become run down and whose digestion may become sluggish, *Erythraea* will perk up the appetite and can play a large part in restoring lost vitality. In short, for anyone who needs a pick-me-up, but is not strong enough for the more bracing tonics, *Erythraea* is a friend in need.

## Cultivation

*Erythraea* is a fairly common wildflower in its native habitat, but it is not easy to grow. For medicinal use, the herb is still collected from the wild. The leaves can be picked from July to September.

**ALSO KNOWN AS:**
*Centaurium erythraea*

**FAMILY:**
*Gentianaceae*

**COMMON ENGLISH NAMES:**
*Centaury*

**ORIGIN:**
*Europe and North Africa*

**MAIN USES:**
*Medicinal*

**PARTS USED:**
*Aerial parts*

# ESCHSCHOLZIA CALIFORNICA

*E*schscholzia is related to the opium poppy (*Papaver somniferum*), and contains some similar alkaloids – but much less powerful, and not addictive. Gentle enough to be given to children who are hyperactive or who cannot sleep, *Eschscholzia* is also useful to adults who suffer from insomnia or who are over-anxious. It can be used in two ways. The first is as a straightforward, sleep-inducing remedy to be taken last thing at night, and again if you wake before morning, in which case it could be combined with *Passiflora*, *Lactuca* or perhaps *Humulus*.

The second way, which can go further towards dealing with the root causes of sleeplessness, is to take calming herbs like *Eschscholzia*, together with herbs, such as *Avena*, *Verbena* and *Hypericum*, that nourish and strengthen the nervous system, during the day on a regular basis. Once you are stronger, night-time problems often resolve themselves. *Eschscholzia* also helps with day-time problems such as anxiety and panic attacks.

*Eschscholzia* has a gently anodyne effect, although it is not nearly as effective as *Papaver somniferum* at dealing with pain. However, it can help in taking the edge off pain, and in easing the anxiety that goes with it.

## Cultivation

The cheerful, bright orange flowers make *Eschscholzia* a popular garden plant. It is a fairly easy annual, liking sunshine and tolerating a dry soil. The herb is collected at the time of flowering, between June and September.

**FAMILY:**
*Papaveraceae*

**COMMON ENGLISH NAMES:**
*California poppy*

**ORIGIN:**
*North America; now widely cultivated*

**MAIN USES:**
*Medicinal*

**PARTS USED:**
*Aerial parts*

# EUCALYPTUS GLOBULUS AND SPP.

A great many members of the *Eucalyptus* family can be used medicinally. The leaves can be infused as a tea or used to make a poultice, but it is the oil distilled from them that is used most. Eucalyptus oil is powerfully antiseptic, and has a penetrating quality that can help to unblock sinuses and get to work on chest infections. Made into a poultice or an ointment and applied to the chest, it has become a standard remedy for the problems of catarrh and congestion that are particularly prevalent in colder and damper climates. The oil can also be breathed in via a hot inhalation, or put in an oil burner to diffuse slowly into the air. This can be especially

**FAMILY:**
*Compositae*

**COMMON ENGLISH NAMES:**
*Eucalyptus, blue gum tree, stringy bark tree*

**ORIGIN:**
*Australia; now very widespread*

**MAIN USES:**
*Medicinal, perfume*

**PARTS USED:**
*Leaves*

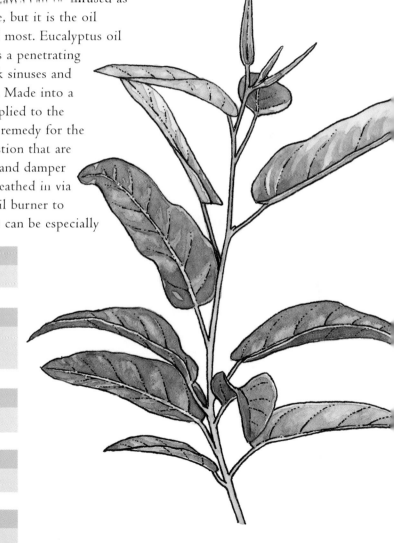

useful at night. It can be mixed with other decongestant oils such as
*Pinus sylvestris* (pine), *Thymus vulgaris* (thyme) and *Mentha piperita*
(peppermint).

*Eucalyptus'* main use is for sinusitis – acute or chronic – colds and
chest complaints, but it is also a deterrent to biting insects if applied
in diluted form to the skin, and helps with skin parasites like scabies.

## Other
The oil of *Eucalyptus citriodora*, the lemon-scented gum, is used in
perfumery.

## Cultivation

*Eucalyptus* has been successfully introduced into southern Europe, Africa, India, America and many other places, and is so successful that it has become something of a pest, often crowding out indigenous trees. It will grow anywhere as long as there is no more than a touch of frost, and can reach great heights. Not for small gardens!

One of the reasons *Eucalyptus* has been so widely planted is that it dries out the soil where it is grown, as well as deterring pests and making the air healthier with the antiseptic fragrance of its leaves. Places that used to be uninhabitable due to malaria have been made safe for people to live in because of the presence of *Eucalyptus*.

# EUPHRASIA OFFICINALIS

The name 'eyebright' not only describes what the herb does but also how it looks, scattered in grassy places like little bright eyes. Since the Middle Ages at least, *Euphrasia officinalis* and its European close cousins have been regarded as specifics for any kind of eye problems, from sore eyes to blindness.

In fact, *Euphrasia* is tonic to the mucus membranes, so it works not just on the eyes but also on inflammation and congestion in the sinuses, nose and ears. Euphrasia can be used for any catarrhal condition in the upper respiratory tract, including allergic rhinitis, or hay fever, together with complementary herbs like *Solidago* (golden rod), *Verbascum* (mullein) or *Echinacea*. It is particularly helpful in dealing with glue ear in children, caused by repeated infections and treatment with antibiotics.

For the eyes themselves, *Euphrasia* has been found to work well on conditions such as conjunctivitis and blepharitis, either taken internally or used as a compress. An infusion of *Euphrasia* can be used to make an eyebath, but it must be strained through fine cloth to ensure that there are no particles of herb left in the liquid.

## Cultivation

*Euphrasia* grows wild on heath and moors, especially on dry and chalky soils. It is semi-parasitic, getting part of its nourishment from the roots of nearby grasses, so it must be grown with grass if it is to flourish.

**FAMILY:**
*Scrophulariaceae*

**COMMON ENGLISH NAMES:**
*Eyebright*

**ORIGIN:**
*Britain*

**MAIN USES:**
*Medicinal*

**PARTS USED:**
*Aerial parts*

# FILIPENDULA ULMARIA

*F*ilipendula is a valuable remedy for most digestive troubles, from heartburn and acid reflux, stomach ulcers and inflammation to loose bowels. It contains salicylic acid, a potent anti-inflammatory that is the active ingredient in aspirin. However, there is no danger of causing irritation to the stomach lining, which is a major drawback of using aspirin or the other NSAIDS (non-steroidal anti-inflammatory drugs). On the contrary, the full spectrum of constituents in *Filipendula* makes it a reliable stomach healer; an excellent example of the way in which a whole remedy can be beneficial in a way that its separate components are not. It reduces stomach acid, protects and heals the stomach lining, and is

**FAMILY:**
*Rosaceae*

**COMMON ENGLISH NAMES:**
*Meadowsweet, queen of the meadow*

**ORIGIN:**
*Europe*

**MAIN USES:**
*Medicinal*

**PARTS USED:**
*Aerial parts*

gently astringent to the intestine. Use it with *Glycyrrhiza, Matricaria, Melissa* or *Symphytum*.

*Filipendula*'s salicylic acid content makes it useful for those suffering from rheumatic pains in the joints and muscles, and it can also help to bring down a fever. Combine it with *Glycyrrhiza, Dioscorea villosa* (wild yam) or *Harpagophytum* for rheumatism, and *Achillea, Sambucus* and *Nepeta cataria* (catmint) for fevers.

## Culinary
It is still sometimes used to flavour meads and beers.

## Other
The flowers, which have an almond-like scent, and the leaves, which are also sweetly fragrant, were both used as strewing herbs in former times, and the smell of them was said to 'make the heart merrie and joyful and delight the senses'.

## Cultivation
*Filipendula* is a herb of riverbanks, damp pastures and hedges if there is water nearby. More like a bride than a queen of the meadow, its frothing masses of creamy-white, intensely scented flowers bloom from June until August.

# FOENICULUM VULGARE

This is one of the many members of the Umbelliferae family that are valuable for their digestive properties. Gentle enough to be used in gripe water for babies, yet strong enough to be a valuable antidote to indigestion and irritable bowel for adults, *Foeniculum* also improves the taste of herbal mixtures. It can be used with *Glycyrrhiza*, *Symphytum*, *Taraxacum radix* or *Matricaria*.

*Foeniculum* is found in cough remedies, both for its flavour and for its antispasmodic action, and it makes a good companion for *Euphrasia* in treating conjunctivitis and blepharitis. Finally, it is one of many herbs that can help to stimulate milk production in breastfeeding mothers.

**FAMILY:**
*Umbelliferae*

**COMMON ENGLISH NAMES:**
*Fennel*

**ORIGIN:**
*Temperate Europe; now naturalised in many places*

**MAIN USES:**
*Medicinal, culinary, perfume*

**PARTS USED:**
*Seeds*

## Culinary

*Foeniculum* has been eaten as a green vegetable since Roman times, and is still used in salads, soups and sauces. There is also a variety cultivated for its bulbous 'roots', which are actually the swollen bases of the leaves. However, it is probably most used in seed form to flavour all kinds of dishes, as well as cordials and liqueurs. In Europe, it was a traditional companion to fish, both white and oily, as its flavour complements the taste of the fish, while its aromatic oil makes the fish more digestible.

## Other

*Foeniculum* oil is used to make perfumes and soaps.

## Cultivation

*Foeniculum* likes a dry soil, especially on limestone, and plenty of sun. Once a plant is established, it should last for many years. If the flower-heads are removed, the plant will provide green shoots throughout the season, but if seeds are required it should be allowed to flower in July and August. The umbels are harvested when the seeds are ripe, and threshed out after drying.

# FUCUS VESICULOSUS

The most useful property of *Fucus* is that it is rich in iodine. Iodine is required for the healthy working of the thyroid gland, which drives, or at least influences, most of the processes of the body. An underactive thyroid gland results in a general slowing down; the sufferer has less energy, may feel depressed and sleep more and tends to gain weight. If the thyroid gland is overactive, the opposite is true. *Fucus* seems to help restore balance, whichever way it has swung, although it is more often used to 'feed' an underactive thyroid gland. Even if blood tests show that the thyroid is functioning within normal limits, *Fucus* can act as a tonic or pick-up for someone whose energy is low, especially if they have been coping with stress for a long time. It works well with *Avena*, *Verbena* and *Glycyrrhiza* in this way.

Like all seaweeds, *Fucus* is a useful bulk laxative, as it goes on absorbing moisture after being eaten, and gently stimulates the bowel. It can be used as part of a detoxifying programme in this way, together with herbs like *Calendula*, *Taraxacum* and *Urtica*, for example.

## Other

Where it is plentiful *Fucus* is used as a manure, as it is a rich source of potash.

## Caution

Like other seaweeds, *Fucus* can absorb heavy metals

**FAMILY:**
Fucaceae

**COMMON ENGLISH NAMES:**
Kelp, bladder wrack

**ORIGIN:**
North Atlantic Ocean

**MAIN USES:**
Medicinal

**PARTS USED:**
Whole plant (thallus)

and other potentially toxic waste. Commercial stocks are tested periodically to ensure that they are 'clean', but if you are gathering your own, choose a stretch of coastline that is not affected by any spillages or industrial outflows.

## Cultivation

*Fucus* is a common seaweed, and is gathered along the seashore where it grows at the end of June. *Fucus* gathered later in the year will not keep for long. Loose plants cannot be used medicinally because once they are detached they lose some of their useful constituents.

# FUMARIA OFFICINALIS

*F*umaria is a bitter herb, tonic to the liver and gall bladder, and both laxative and diuretic. All these actions contribute to its reputation as a 'blood cleanser', an old-fashioned term for herbs that support the body's processes of elimination. Its main uses nowadays are twofold.

The first is as a normaliser for the gall bladder, together with herbs like *Berberis vulgaris*, *Taraxacum radix* and *Carduus marianus*. It can relieve the pain of biliary colic, and migraines relating to biliary problems. The second, which also stems from its cleansing properties, is in helping to clear skin conditions such as eczema and acne. For this purpose it works well with *Rumex*, *Glycyrrhiza* and *Calendula*, among others.

## Other
The flowers can be used to make a yellow dye for wool.

## Cultivation
*Fumaria* is a common weed, in the wild and in the flowerbed. It flowers throughout the summer, and can be collected during this time. It is not usually deliberately planted in the garden, as it tends to become a nuisance, but like many weeds, it flourishes in rich, well-fed soil.

**FAMILY:**
*Fumariaceae*

**COMMON ENGLISH NAMES:**
*Fumitory, earth smoke*

**ORIGIN:**
*Europe; now naturalised in USA and elsewhere*

**MAIN USES:**
*Medicinal*

**PARTS USED:**
*Aerial parts*

FAMILY
*Rubiaceae*

COMMON ENGLISH NAMES:
*Cleavers, Clivers, Goose Grass*

ORIGIN:
*Europe and North America*

MAIN USES:
*Medicinal*

PARTS USED:
*Aerial parts*

# GALIUM APERINE

*Galium aperine* is known, first and foremost, for its ability to support and cleanse the lymphatic system. Thus, whenever swollen glands are a problem, *G. aperime* is indicated, used with other herbs depending on what is causing the swelling. It is particularly valuable in tonsillitis and adenoid trouble. If infection is present, use it with *Echinacea, Calendula* or *Phytolacca decandra* (poke root). Where the glands have become chronically swollen, often due to repeated infections that may have been treated with antibiotics, which kill micro-organisms but do not help the clearing up process afterwards, *G. aperime* will slowly but surely encourage them to flow freely again. It is very gentle and may be taken by children, for as long as is needed.

Traditionally, *G. aperime* has also been used to treat ulcers and tumours, and it finds a place in anti-cancer prescriptions. In such cases, of course, herbs must only be used with professional advice.

## Cultivation

*G. aperime* is a very common hedgerow weed, often found growing near nettles; the two are quick to colonise disturbed ground, and spread fast. Gather it in May and June when it is just coming into flower.

# GALIUM VERUM

This herb was used in much the same way as *Galium aparine*, but it is much less abundant, and so less well known.

## Culinary

One of its names, cheese rennet, refers to its ability to curdle milk. It was traditionally used to make cheese in many areas. The rich yellow colour of Cheshire cheese was due to *Galium verum*, although the colour is now produced by adding annatto.

## Other

The English name, lady's redstraw, refers to its use as a stuffing for mattresses, as well as for strewing on the floor. Even fine ladies were said to prefer it. The stems and leaves yield a yellow dye.

**FAMILY:**
*Rubiaceae*

**COMMON ENGLISH NAMES:**
*Lady's bedstraw, cheese rennet*

**ORIGIN:**
*Northern Europe*

**MAIN USES:**
*Medicinal*

**PARTS USED:**
*Aerial parts*

## Cultivation

*Galium verum* is a wildflower of dry banks and hedges, especially near the sea. The yellow flowers appear in July and August.

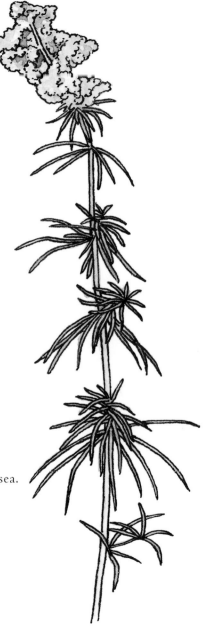

# GINKGO BILOBA

*G*inkgo is a gentle but powerful circulatory stimulant, especially useful for conditions affecting the head. It helps to prevent arteriosclerosis, which makes it an invaluable remedy for older people, particularly those who have suffered strokes or are at risk of them. *Ginkgo* can safely be taken continuously, along with such herbs as *Panax ginseng* (if appropriate), *Rosmarinus* and *Tilia*.

*Ginkgo* can help to improve the memory and sharpen concentration in people of any age, but it has attracted attention recently for its ability to help the elderly confused, and perhaps to delay or mitigate the ravages of Alzheimer's disease. It is also well known in the treatment of tinnitus, dizziness, labyrinthitis and Meniere's disease. Finally, it is well

**FAMILY:**
*Ginkgoaceae*

**COMMON ENGLISH NAMES:**
*Ginkgo, maidenhair tree*

**ORIGIN:**
*China*

**MAIN USES:**
*Medicinal, culinary*

**PARTS USED:**
*Leaves*

worth trying for persistent headaches and migraines.

## Culinary
The seeds can be eaten like nuts.

## Caution
If you are taking blood-thinning drugs, or any other medication for the treatment or prevention of stroke, make sure that your doctor is informed if you want to take *Ginkgo* as well. It is a very useful ally, but may affect the dosage of drugs that are needed.

## Cultivation
Now often grown in gardens, *Ginkgo* is grown from ripe seed. It flourishes in well-drained, humus-rich soil in a sunny position, but its growth rate is erratic from year to year. *Ginkgo* trees can live to a great age.

# GLYCYRRHIZA GLABRA

*Glycyrrhiza* has long been used in medicines to disguise unpleasant tastes, but its virtues go much further than that. Traditionally, it was a favourite ingredient in cough mixtures, adding its soothing, anti-inflammatory action, and stimulating the flow of mucus from the lungs and bronchi. It works well with *Thymus*, *Inula* and *Echinacea*, for example. The same soothing action is used to heal gastritis and peptic ulcers; before the advent of modern drugs like Zantac, it was the medication of choice for orthodox doctors as well as herbalists. It can be combined with *Symphytum*, *Filipendula* or *Althaea* for these conditions.

*Glycyrrhiza* contains substances that are very similar to the body's own steroids, and it can be used to treat all sorts of conditions that would respond to steroidal drugs, such as arthritis, ulcerative colitis, eczema or any other condition involving runaway inflammation. Its action is not so strong, but it does not have the undesirable long-term side effects of steroid use. This is partly because the natural steroids contained in it are balanced and buffered by all the other constituents, but also because it acts to support and strengthen the adrenal gland, unlike steroidal drugs which tend to depress its action. So, besides being useful for actual diseases of the adrenal gland, it helps to restore it to full function when someone has had to take steroids.

For arthritis, it could be used with *Harpagophytum*, *Apium* and *Symphytum*. For ulcerative

**FAMILY:**
*Leguminosae*

**COMMON ENGLISH NAMES:**
*Liquorice*

**ORIGIN:**
*South-east Europe and South-west Asia*

**MAIN USES:**
*Medicinal, culinary*

**PARTS USED:**
*Root*

colitis and Crohn's disease, combine it with *Chamomilla, Melissa,* and *Symphytum.* For eczema, try it with *Trifolium, Rumex* and *Viola.* As always, consult a professional if you do not get good results within six weeks or so.

## Culinary

*Glycyrrhiza* means 'sweet root' in Greek, and certainly the herb has been prized for its sweet taste since classical times. It is made into confectionery in many forms, and added to tobacco, both for smoking and chewing. It is also added to some beers, notably porter and stout, to make them thicker and blacker.

## Caution

It should not be used by anyone suffering from high blood pressure.

## Cultivation

*Glycyrrhiza* needs a deep, well-fed soil. Runners from old plants are planted in late autumn or early spring. The roots are ready for harvest after three years, and are dug in late autumn.

# HUMULUS LUPULUS

The main use of *Humulus* is as a mild sedative. It can help to ease anxiety and tension, calm restlessness and bring peaceful sleep. It is also calming to the digestive system, and can help with indigestion and irritable bowel. For this, try it with *Chamomilla* and *Symphytum*. To treat anxiety, use it with *Valeriana* or *Passiflora*. To help with insomnia, combine it with *Passiflora*, *Lactuca* or *Eschscholzia*.

*Humulus* is one of the many herbs that contain plant oestrogens, and it can be a useful friend to women going through the menopause. The oestrogen content is probably what gives it a reputation (for men) of dampening sexual desire – not an aspect of beer-drinking that is widely advertised!

**FAMILY:**
*Cannabinaceae*

**COMMON ENGLISH NAMES:**
*Hops*

**ORIGIN:**
*Northern temperate countries*

**MAIN USES:**
*Medicinal, culinary*

**PARTS USED:**
*Flowers of female plant (strobiles)*

## Culinary

*Humulus* has been an essential ingredient in beer in Europe since the Middle Ages, and it is now grown in suitable conditions worldwide for this purpose. The young shoots used to be valued as a vegetable in Roman times.

## Other

The leaves and flower-heads have been used to produce a brown dye.

## Caution

*Humulus* is not suitable for people suffering from depression.

## Cultivation

*Humulus* needs a deep, rich soil and sunshine. Plants are taken from cuttings and planted in October or November, but do not come into full bearing until the third year. The strobiles are gathered before they are fully ripe, in August and September, and must not be overheated when drying.

# HYPERICUM PERFORATUM

*H*ypericum is a useful wound healer, especially for burns – including sunburn – bruises and varicose veins. It can be applied in a cream base or made into an infusion as a wash. Alternatively, an infused oil can be made by steeping the herb in vegetable oil for several weeks in sunshine.

Taken internally, *Hypericum* is a sovereign remedy for depression and anxiety. It is safe for long-term use, but should not be combined with certain anti-depressants. It is highly effective in mild depression, and carries no unwanted side effects. This is the use that has carried the herb to superstardom in the last decade or so. Combine it with *Passiflora*, *Scutellaria* or *Avena*, among others. *Hypericum* is a faithful ally to those going through changes of any kind, and is

**FAMILY:**

*Hypericaceae*

**COMMON ENGLISH NAMES:**

*St.John's wort*

**ORIGIN:**

*Europe and Asia*

**MAIN USES:**

*Medicinal*

**PARTS USED:**

*Herb tops and flowers*

particularly well known as a helper during the menopause.

*Hypericum* is also useful for physical problems of the nervous system, such as neuralgia after shingles, trigeminal neuralgia, and conditions in which inflamed or irritated nerves play a part, such as carpal tunnel syndrome, repetitive strain injury and sciatica.

## Caution

*Hypericum* should not be used in conjunction with various anti-depressants and other prescription drugs, as it can affect their uptake and metabolism. If you are on any medication, check with your doctor or herbalist before taking *Hypericum* as well.

## Cultivation

*Hypericum* is not uncommon in woods, hedges, and meadows, but its huge popularity in recent years means that most commercial preparations will be from cultivated stock. It is perennial, not hard to grow, and the flowers, or the whole herb if required, are gathered when in bloom at midsummer.

# HYSSOPUS OFFICINALIS

Like its close relative *Thymus vulgaris* (thyme), *Hyssopus* is a useful remedy for coughs, colds and chronic catarrh, as well as for lower respiratory problems like bronchitis and pneumonia. This is largely due to its volatile oil content, which helps to kill off infections, stimulate the flow of mucus in the nasal and bronchial passages, and soothe spasm and inflammation. It is also gently sedative, so where anxiety is a factor — in chronic asthma, for instance, and for sick children — it is well worth a try. Combine it with *Glycyrrhiza*, *Angelica archangelica* and *Inula helenium* for coughs and bronchitis, with *Sambucus*, *Mentha piperita* and *Echinacea* for colds and catarrh, and — under professional guidance — herbs such as *Ephedra sinica*, *Euphorbia pilulifera* and *Drosera rotundifolia* for asthma.

*Hyssopus* has a further specific use in the management of *petit mal* epilepsy, arising from its

| FAMILY: |
|---|
| *Labiatae* |

| COMMON ENGLISH NAMES: |
|---|
| *Hyssop* |

| ORIGIN: |
|---|
| *Southern Europe* |

| MAIN USES: |
|---|
| *Medicinal, perfume* |

| PARTS USED: |
|---|
| *Aerial parts* |

calming antispasmodic action. Again, professional guidance is needed, but in mild cases it can help to keep the condition under control.

## Culinary

*Hyssopus* is an ingredient in many liqueurs, of which Chartreuse is probably the best known. Bees love *Hyssopus*, and the honey produced from it has a fine flavour.

## Other

Hyssop oil is used in perfumery.

## Cultivation

*Hyssopus* likes sunshine and dry soil, and will not thrive in damp places. It is evergreen, easily grown from seed, and the herb is gathered when in flower in August. The beautiful dark blue flowers are a favourite with bees.

# INULA HELENIUM

*Inula* is a specific for irritating coughs, whether the cough arises from asthma, infection, chronic bronchitis, emphysema or causes unknown. In the past, it played its part in the treatment of tuberculosis. It has a unique combination of ingredients that soothe inflammation, stimulate mucus to flow, discourage infection and have a tonic effect both on the lungs and on the digestive system.

This means that *Inula* is also useful for people recovering from illness, and can be very valuable in treating chronic fatigue. One of its English names, 'elf dock', refers to the belief that it would heal anyone who had been shot by elves – this would cause the victim to lose vitality and waste away.

Suitable for both children and adults, it can be taken for as long as is necessary. For coughs, combine it with herbs such as *Glycyrrhiza*, *Hyssopus*, *Echinacea* or *Achillea*. For convalescence and chronic

**FAMILY:**
*Compositae*

**COMMON ENGLISH NAMES:**
*Elecampane, elf dock*

**ORIGIN:**
*Europe and temperate Asia;
naturalised in eastern USA*

**MAIN USES:**
*Medicinal*

**PARTS USED:**
*Rhizome*

fatigue, try it with *Avena, Verbena* or *Taraxacum radix.*

## Culinary

*Inula* roots used to be grown in the kitchen garden, to be candied and eaten as a sweet – just for pleasure or to help with coughs and indigestion. In Switzerland, it is one of the traditional ingredients of absinthe.

## Cultivation

*Inula* is a giant daisy, too big for a small garden; think Sunflower-sized. It grows wild, preferring moist and shady places, producing bright yellow flowers from June to August. The roots are dug between September and October, and need to be cut up before drying.

# JUNIPERUS COMMUNIS

*Juniperus* is useful both inside and out. Taken internally, it is a good remedy for cystitis, so long as there is no kidney disease present (it is quite stimulating to the kidney nephrons, which is beneficial as long as they are functioning normally). Use it, for example, with *Agropyron*, *Zea* and *Arctostaphylos*.

Externally, the oil is very effective at easing the aches and pains of rheumatism, arthritis, and muscular problems. Combined with other oils such as *Rosmarinus officinalis*, *Myrtus communis* and *Cinnamonum zeylanicum*, either in a neutral oil base (to make a lotion or massage oil) or as a cream (to

**FAMILY:**

*Coniferae*

**COMMON ENGLISH NAMES:**

*Juniper*

**ORIGIN:**

*Europe, North Africa, North Asia and North America*

**MAIN USES:**

*Medicinal*

**PARTS USED:**

*Berries and leaves*

rub into the skin), it can be part of a management strategy. It is useful as first aid for injuries and acute rheumatic flare-ups, but if you use it regularly it will help to prevent flare-ups and keep the joints well oiled.

## Culinary
The oil from the berries is an essential ingredient of Jenever, or Dutch gin. It has also been used to flavour beer.

## Caution
*Juniperus* should not be taken in pregnancy. It should also be avoided in kidney disease, and is best taken for no more than six weeks or so at a time.

## Cultivation
*Juniperus* is a common wild shrub, especially on chalk-bearing soils in upland areas, and does best on sunny slopes. The berries take two or three years to ripen, and only the ripe berries, which are blue in colour, should be picked in the autumn.

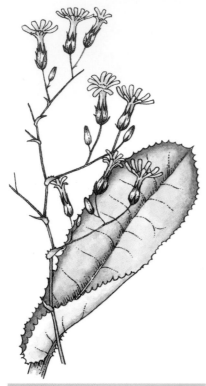

# LACTUCA VIROSA

All the members of the lettuce family contain opiate-like substances that are sedative and pain relieving. A naturopath with whom I worked used to recommend to nervous patients that they eat a whole lettuce every day, but you can get the same effect by taking a medicinal dose of *Lactuca*, as it is much stronger than its domestic relatives (although it tastes much worse!). It is, however, gentle enough for children, and does not depress the digestion like the opiate-based drugs. It calms excitability and nervous tension, and can help children who are hyperactive or who cannot sleep; try it with *Matricaria*, *Melissa* or *Eschscholzia*. For adults, too, it is a valuable remedy for sleeplessness and anxiety; try it with *Passiflora*, *Valeriana* or *Humulus*.

Because *Lactuca* is antispasmodic, it can be used for irritable coughs, colic, and painful periods, and will also ease muscular spasms due to rheumatism or injuries.

## Culinary

*Lactuca* is too bitter to be used as a salad herb, unlike its cousins, the cultivated lettuces.

## Other

The latex used to be sold as 'lettuce opium', but it is definitely a poor relation, and not used nowadays.

## Cultivation

*Lactuca* grows wild in waste places, flowering in July and August. The leaves should be collected before flowering, in June and July. The latex used to be collected by making cuts in the flower-heads, in the same way as from the opium poppy (*Papaver somniferum*).

**FAMILY:**
*Compositae*

**COMMON ENGLISH NAMES:**
*Wild lettuce*

**ORIGIN:**
*Western and Southern Europe*

**MAIN USES:**
*Medicinal*

**PARTS USED:**
*Leaves*

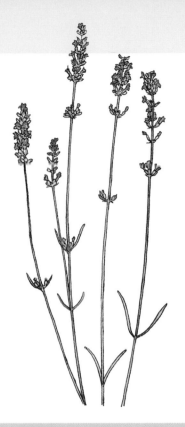

# LAVANDULA OFFICINALIS

O ne of the best known of all herbs, *Lavandula* is not often taken internally these days, though it can be made into a relaxing tea. It is mainly used as an oil, rubbed directly into the skin, added to a bath or inhaled. It is a wonderfully calming and relaxing herb, with a strong first-aid effect; dabbed on the temples, it can relieve a headache, and it will relieve earache in seconds if dropped into the affected ear. Used regularly, it can help to relieve depression and calm anxiety, and so helps when someone is in a state of nervous exhaustion.

## Culinary

*Lavendula* was used as a condiment or conserve, but has yet to come back into fashion for eating.

FAMILY:
*Labiatae*

COMMON ENGLISH NAMES:
*Lavender*

ORIGIN:
*Western Mediterranean; now widely grown*

MAIN USES:
*Medicinal, perfume*

PARTS USED:
*Flowers, perfume*

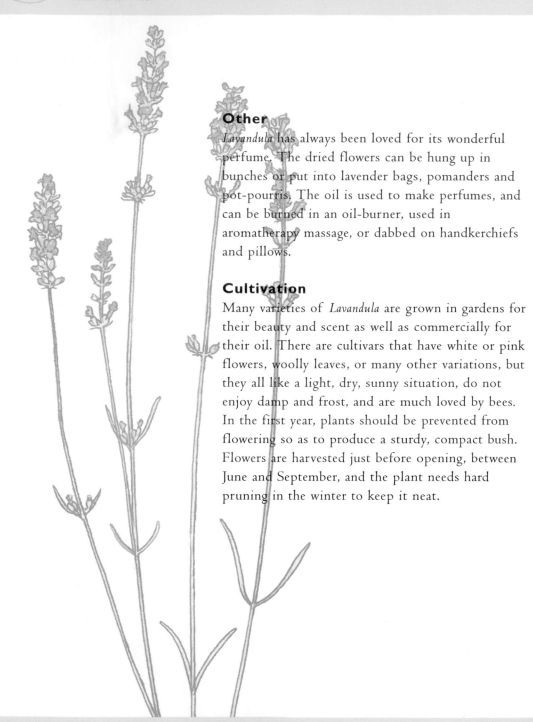

## Other

*Lavandula* has always been loved for its wonderful perfume. The dried flowers can be hung up in bunches or put into lavender bags, pomanders and pot-pourris. The oil is used to make perfumes, and can be burned in an oil-burner, used in aromatherapy massage, or dabbed on handkerchiefs and pillows.

## Cultivation

Many varieties of *Lavandula* are grown in gardens for their beauty and scent as well as commercially for their oil. There are cultivars that have white or pink flowers, woolly leaves, or many other variations, but they all like a light, dry, sunny situation, do not enjoy damp and frost, and are much loved by bees. In the first year, plants should be prevented from flowering so as to produce a sturdy, compact bush. Flowers are harvested just before opening, between June and September, and the plant needs hard pruning in the winter to keep it neat.

# LEONURUS CARDIACA

The Latin name, *cardiaca*, indicates that *Leonurus* has a long history of use for heart complaints, both physical and emotional. Nowadays it is mainly used when there is anxiety leading to heart symptoms such as palpitations and missed beats. On an emotional level, the old writers say that it strengthens and gladdens the heart and drives out melancholy – a useful part of many herbal tonics. It works well with *Crataegus*, *Valeriana* and *Passiflora*.

The English name, 'motherwort', is a clue to the herb's other main use. It helps to normalise the menstrual cycle, especially when anxiety may be a factor in missing periods, and can ease tension when a woman is having false labour pains. Most of all, it has a part to play in easing the symptoms of the menopause, the hot flushes and mood swings that can make life miserable. Try it with *Salvia*, *Calendula* and *Achillea*.

## Cultivation

Once you have it in your garden, it will spread seed year by year. The plants are unfussy and will live for many years. Cut and dry the herb from June to September, when it is in flower.

**FAMILY:**
*Labiatae*

**COMMON ENGLISH NAMES:**
*Motherwort*

**ORIGIN:**
*Europe*

**MAIN USES:**
*Medicinal*

**PARTS USED:**
*Aerial parts*

# LINUM USITATISSIMUM

*L*inum seed can absorb many times its own weight in water, and this is the quality most used in healing. Taken internally, it is a bulk laxative, gently encouraging the bowels to move without irritating or forcing the process, making it a much better long-term remedy for constipation than the more stimulating laxatives like *Cassia*. Combine it with digestives like *Zingiber*, *Carum* or *Foeniculum*. Pour a cup of boiling water onto 2–3 teaspoonfuls of seeds, and leave for 10–15 minutes. Drink the remedy morning and evening.

Externally, *Linum* is a wonderful base for a

FAMILY:
*Linaceae*

COMMON ENGLISH NAMES:
*Linseed, flax*

ORIGIN:
*Widespread in temperate and tropical areas*

MAIN USES:
*Medicinal, craft*

PARTS USED:
*Seed*

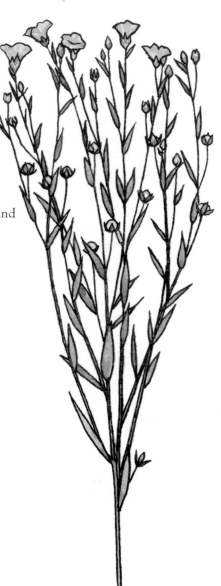

poultice, wherever there is inflammation or a wound needs drawing. For chest infections, infected wounds and splinters, and for skin problems such as boils, carbuncles and shingles, use it with other soothing herbs like *Althaea radix* and *Ulmus fulva*. To this base you can add various herbs, depending on the action you require: *Brassica* where heat is needed; *Calendula* to clear infection; and *Avena* to cool and soothe inflammation.

To make a poultice, soak enough ground or crushed seeds in water to make a paste. Spread this on a piece of muslin or other thin cloth, and turn the edges in to make a parcel. Put a little oil on the skin to stop it sticking, and place the poultice over this. Cover it with something waterproof – clingfilm comes in useful here – and put a hot-water bottle on top to keep it warm.

## Culinary
Linseed is occasionally mixed with wheat grain for bread making, but in general it is seen as medicinal rather than something to be eaten for pleasure.

## Other
*Linum* has been used since ancient times to make linen cloth, rope, sacking, sails and fishnets.

Linseed oil is used to 'feed' wooden articles and keep them from drying out; cricket bats are the most famous example. It dries to a thin varnish, and so can be mixed with paint and ink to improve their drying qualities.

## Cultivation

*Linum* requires a very rich soil, and does not like clay or gravel. Seed is sown for field crops in March or April. The plants must be harvested just after flowering in August, if grown for making linen, but if grown for seed, the seed pods are gathered when fully ripe in September.

# LIPPIA CITRIODORA

O ne of the many herbs that strengthen the digestion, *Lippia* both stimulates the stomach and calms indigestion and flatulence. If taken strong enough, it will provoke a sweat, which makes it a favourite tea for cooling and refreshing in hot summer weather.

## Culinary

One of those herbs that crosses the divide between food and medicine, *Lippia* is most used as a tea or tisane, either on its own or mixed with other pleasant-tasting herbs.

## Other

*Lippia* has a fresh, lemony fragrance, which is due to its essential-oil content. This is highly valued in perfumery. The leaves keep their scent for many years, so they are a useful ingredient of pot-pourris, pomanders and linen sachets, which can be placed in clothes drawers to keep their contents smelling fresh and to deter moths.

## Cultivation

*Lippia* is a deciduous shrub, up to 1.5 metres tall, with very fragrant leaves. It is not very hardy, and needs a sheltered situation, preferably frost-free. It is gathered when in flower in August.

FAMILY:

*Verbenaceae*

COMMON ENGLISH NAMES:

*Lemon verbena*

ORIGIN:

*Chile and Peru*

MAIN USES:

*Medicinal, culinary, perfume*

PARTS USED:

*Leaves and flowering tops*

# MATRICARIA CHAMOMILLA

*M*atricaria is one of the herbal all-rounders, useful in prescriptions for all sorts of problems. It will calm anxiety and relax tension, both physical and emotional. It is very useful for children who are hyperactive or have trouble sleeping. Use it with other calming herbs like *Tilia*, *Lactuca* or *Scutellaria*. It will also calm and heal digestive troubles such as gastritis, peptic ulcers and irritable bowel, and indigestion of any sort. For mouth ulcers and sore throats, try it as a gargle, perhaps with *Salvia* or *Calendula*.

**ALSO CALLED:**
*Matricaria recutita or Chamomilla matricaria*

**FAMILY:**
*Compositae*

**COMMON ENGLISH NAMES:**
*German chamomile, wild chamomile*

**ORIGIN:**
*Europe, North Africa and temperate Asia*

**MAIN USES:**
*Medicinal, culinary*

**PARTS USED:**
*Flowers*

On the skin, *Matricaria* speeds up wound healing and soothes inflammation. Use it for minor wounds, sunburn and inflamed eczema, with companions like *Symphytum*, *Calendula* or *Aloe*. It can also be used to bathe sore and inflamed eyes, along with *Euphrasia* or *Foeniculum*.

## Culinary

*Matricaria* makes a pleasant tea, and is often drunk without reference to its healing qualities – although not everybody likes the taste.

## Other

Known as the 'Plants' Physician', *Matricaria* will strengthen other plants growing nearby, and can be placed next to sickly plants to aid their recovery.

## Cultivation

*Matricaria* grows wild in its native habitat, and is often found in or near cornfields. The various chamomiles are easily confused, so to be sure of what you have, grow it from seed. It likes sun and light soil. The flowers are gathered between May and August, in dry weather.

# MELALEUCA ALTERNIFOLIA

Melaleuca has one great claim to fame, which has led to an explosion in its use in recent years. Its essential oil, like most others, has anti-inflammatory and anti-infective qualities. When tests were carried out on a number of essential oils, however, it was found to be the most potent anti-microbial of them all. It is not to be taken internally, but when applied to the skin it will kill, or at the very least discourage, all kinds of infections, whether bacterial, viral or fungal. It is gentle enough to be used undiluted, although it is generally incorporated into a cream, which will remain on the skin and allow the oil to be absorbed gradually. It could also be put into an oil base to make eardrops, or made into pessaries to relieve the symptoms of vaginal thrush.

## Culinary

As its common name suggests, Australian settlers used *Melaleuca* as a tea substitute. It is gently stimulating and refreshing, although it contains no caffeine.

## Cultivation

*Melaleuca* is grown commercially in Australia, and cultivation is now being extended to other countries.

FAMILY:

Myrtaceae

COMMON ENGLISH NAMES:

Ti-tree, tea tree

ORIGIN:

Australia

MAIN USES:

Medicinal

PARTS USED:

Leaves

# MELISSA OFFICINALIS

*Melissa* is one of the many digestive herbs, and is a surprisingly strong antispasmodic and wind-dispeller. Like many fragrant herbs, it also acts on the nervous system, calming and cheering. Anyone who regularly takes *Melissa* will cope better with stress. It is particularly good for indigestion where anxiety and tension play a part. For irritable bowel and similar problems, use it with *Symphytum*, *Matricaria* and *Mentha piperita*. For gastritis and stomach ulcers, try it with *Glycyrrhiza*, *Filipendula* and *Althaea*.

Melissa can help to bring down high blood pressure, as it stimulates the circulation at the same time as calming tension. It would combine well with *Crataegus*, *Tilia* or *Achillea*. For anxiety states and mild depression, use it with *Hypericum*, *Valeriana* or *Borago*. *Melissa* is a balm to those who are wounded in spirit, whether by grief or some other kind of trauma.

## Culinary

One of the sweetest-tasting of all herbs, *Melissa* is a popular tea. It can be added to punches and fruit cups for its delicate lemon fragrance.

## Other

*Melissa* means 'bee' in Greek, which indicates that it is one of the best bee-herbs — loved by bees, and loved by humans for the fine honey they make from it. It was traditionally thought that if *Melissa* was grown by the hives, or rubbed onto them, it would not only help the bees to find their way home, but would also attract new ones. Oil of *Melissa* is used in perfumery.

**FAMILY:**

*Labiatae*

**COMMON ENGLISH NAMES:**

*Balm, sweet balm, lemon balm*

**ORIGIN:**

*Southern Europe*

**MAIN USES:**

*Medicinal, culinary, perfume*

**PARTS USED:**

*Aerial parts*

## Cultivation

*Melissa* is a mountain-dweller, and is happiest in light, well-drained soil, but it is vigorous enough to survive almost anywhere. A lovely tea can be made with the fresh leaves and flowers any time from June to October. To harvest it for drying, cut the young shoots when about 30cm long, and you should get three cuts between June and September.

**FAMILY:**

*Labiatae*

**COMMON ENGLISH NAMES:**

*Peppermint*

**ORIGIN:**

*Europe; now widespread*

**MAIN USES:**

*Medicinal*

**PARTS USED:**

*Aerial parts*

# MENTHA PIPERITA

There are many, many members of the *Mentha* family, all of which have been used at some stage in both healing and cookery, but the best for medicinal use is *Mentha piperita*. It is one of our best digestive herbs, combining its wind- and colic-calming actions with a fairly strong painkilling effect and an underlying bitterness that helps to stimulate the flow of digestive juices. Hence, it can be chewed to relieve toothache, or taken to help anything from nausea and vomiting (including pregnancy sickness) to bowel problems like ulcerative colitis and Crohn's disease.

Its other main claim to fame is in the treatment of colds, influenza and catarrh. The oil in *M. piperita* has a penetrating quality, helping to get mucus moving even in chronic sinusitis. Besides being taken internally, it can be inhaled – try it with other oils such as *Eucalyptus*, *Thymus* and *Pinus* – or put into a poultice for chest complaints. It is a cooling herb, and will help to bring down a fever if necessary. For colds and influenza, use it with *Achillea*, *Sambucus* and *Echinacea*.

## Culinary

*Mentha piperita* can be used in cookery, and often is, although *Mentha spicata* (spearmint), is the more usual choice.

## Cultivation

It is a lover of damp places, riverbanks, water meadows and waste ground; *M. piperita* will, however,

tolerate most conditions, as long as the soil is rich enough. It spreads by runners, probably faster than you want it to. Pick the leaves, or cut stems, between July and just before the flowers open.

## Other members of the mentha family

There are now dozens of different cultivars of mentha, as well as the older varieties. It can be variegated or curly, tall and slender or almost invisible (*Mentha requieni*, or Corsican

mint). There are many different scents, including apple, ginger, pineapple and eau de cologne. The one that is still most valued in cookery, however, is *Mentha spicata* (spearmint). Less bitter than *Mentha piperita*, it is no less powerful as a digestive. It can be added to salads, used to garnish cooked vegetables — peas and potatoes are the favourites — and eaten with red meat, particularly lamb, where it helps to digest the fatty and fibrous parts, and marries well with the rich flavour. A little mint in a fruit dessert also helps to give 'point' to the sweeter flavours.

The other well-known member of the family is *Mentha pulegium* (pennyroyal), a creeping mint that is often planted between paving stones or on walls. It was traditionally used to bring on late periods — often a euphemism for a home abortion, always a risky process and not to be recommended.

# MONARDA DIDYMA

The essential oil of *Monarda* is rich in thymol, one of the main active ingredients in *Thymus*. It can be used in similar ways, although it is not nearly as strong, to ease chest complaints and drive out colds. It makes a pleasant and refreshing digestive tea.

## Culinary
*Monarda* used to be popular as a tea in the United States, although it is less so nowadays. The leaves are used in some Thai curries.

## Other
As the name 'bee balm' suggests, *Monarda* is much loved by bees, and is often grown near their hives. The leaves keep their fragrance for a long time, and can be used in pot-pourri or in sachets.

## Caution
*Monarda* can cause a photosensitive reaction. It should not be taken if you are spending a lot of time in the sun.

## Cultivation
Grown for its fresh fragrance and bright scarlet flowers, *Monarda* likes a moist, light soil, and partial shade. Like *Mentha*, it sends out runners, which can be transplanted to increase numbers. Pick the leaves just before flowering.

**FAMILY:**
*Rustaceae*

**COMMON ENGLISH NAMES:**
*Bergamot, bee balm, oswego tea*

**ORIGIN:**
*North America*

**MAIN USES:**
*Medicinal, culinary, perfume*

**PARTS USED:**
*Aerial parts*

# MYRISTICA FRAGRANS

Myristica is a pleasant digestive with a slightly sedative aspect; it makes a useful nightcap, sprinkled into a hot honey and lemon or hot milk drink, for those who cannot sleep. It helps to dispel nausea, and can be used to offset sickness when someone is using nausea-inducing drugs.

Added in small amounts to food and to drinks, Myristica is a valuable herb for convalescents, both stimulating the appetite and helping to allay the irritability that often comes with slow recovery.

## Culinary

At one time in Europe, nutmegs were so highly prized that they were literally worth their weight in gold. Mace has a gentler, mellower taste than nutmeg, but both are used in much the same way. They flavour food, make it more digestible, and help to sterilise it by killing or deterring potentially harmful micro-organisms – more useful in times when there was no refrigeration, but still a valuable quality.

Myristica is used in both savoury and sweet dishes. In particular, it complements cheese and milk, and the cabbage family of vegetables.

| | |
|---|---|
| FAMILY: | *Myristicaceae* |
| COMMON ENGLISH NAMES: | *Nutmeg, mace* |
| ORIGIN: | *Malayan islands; cultivated in Sumatra and French Guiana* |
| MAIN USES: | *Medicinal, culinary* |
| PARTS USED: | *Fruit* |

## Caution

An overdose of *Myristica* can cause nightmares or hallucinations. Do not use more than a pinch of grated nutmeg at a time.

## Cultivation

The fruits mature after about nine years. They can then be gathered up to three times a year. The mace is the outer covering of the fruit, and is dried separately from the kernels. Oil can be extracted, or the nutmegs sold whole or ground.

# MYRTUS COMMUNIS

A good herbal all-rounder, *Myrtus* is attractive, has a lovely scent and offers many gifts, both for healing and eating. Made into a tea, the leaves ease flatulence. They also promote the flow of mucus from the bronchi and nasal passages, and are mildly antibiotic, so helping to get rid of colds and chest complaints.

The oil is quite strongly anti-inflammatory and warming, and is useful in easing rheumatic and arthritic pain. Mix it with a cream or oil base and massage into the affected areas. It goes well with other warming oils like *Juniperus*, *Rosmarinus* and *Cinnamomum*.

## Culinary

*Myrtus* berries are edible, and have been used in the past to sweeten the breath. They can be dried and used as a spice.

## Other

In ancient Greece, Olympic winners were crowned with *Myrtus*. The oil is used in cosmetics and perfumes, and the leaves can be added to pot-pourri.

## Cultivation

*Myrtus* is a tall shrub, reaching 3–5 metres in height. It can be grown outside its native habitat as long as it is protected from frost and cold winds. The leaves have a strong fragrance, and can be gathered, alone or with the flowers, from May to August.

FAMILY:
*Myrtaceae*

COMMON ENGLISH NAMES:
*Myrtle*

ORIGIN:
*Southern Europe and Southeast Asia*

MAIN USES:
*Medicinal, perfume*

PARTS USED:
*Leaves and flowers*

# NASTURTIUM OFFICINALE

The healing virtues of *Nasturtium* are shown by the ways in which people have used it in the past. Its main use was as a tonic or 'blood cleanser' in the spring, when fresh vegetables were not available in northern countries. Its second use was as an appetite stimulant, provoking the flow of digestive juices and enabling better use – and greater enjoyment – of the foods eaten with it. Both of these uses are still valid. *Nasturtium* is a good food for convalescents and anorexics, and a useful source of vitamins at any time.

## Culinary

*Nasturtium* has a pungent, peppery taste. As a salad, it makes a good appetiser, alone or mixed with less strong-tasting ingredients. It is often made into a refreshing soup. Rich in minerals and vitamins, especially vitamin C, it was highly valued for the prevention of scurvy.

## Cultivation

Watercress grows wild in or near running water, and can be cultivated in similar conditions. It can be picked any time when the leaves are green, but they are at their best for eating before the flowers open. For medicinal use, pick it when it is in flower. If you are gathering it in the wild, be sure not to confuse it with fool's cress, which grows in the same places and looks quite similar, but is poisonous. Take a good flora or a knowledgeable friend with you.

**FAMILY:**
*Tropaeolaceae*

**COMMON ENGLISH NAMES:**
*Watercress*

**ORIGIN:**
*Europe and Asia*

**MAIN USES:**
*Medicinal, culinary*

**PARTS USED:**
*Leaves, flowers*

# NEPETA CATARIA

*N*epeta is a strong diaphoretic. In other words, it will bring on a sweat, and can be used to reduce a fever very quickly. It is a good herb to use for a feverish child, and will combine with herbs like *Sambucus* and *Achillea* for colds, influenza and chest infections. Besides making you sweat, it will also calm you down, which again is very useful when dealing with a sick child. *Nepeta* is a good digestive tonic, which is particularly useful for checking diarrhoea in children.

## Culinary

In times past in Europe, *Nepeta* tea was a popular drink. The young shoots are sometimes used in France as a seasoning.

## Other

The smell of *Nepeta* is very exciting for cats, who will roll on it, eat the leaves and behave rather as if they were drunk. It is often put into toys for them to play with, but once dried, it loses its scent quite quickly.

## Cultivation

*Nepeta* is easily grown in the garden, and is not as moisture-hungry as its close relatives, the mints. Folklore says that cats will attack and destroy transplanted seedlings, but those sown in situ will be ignored. This is because the distinctive smell of *Nepeta* is only released when the leaves are bruised or crushed. Gather it when the flowers are just opening, between June and September.

**FAMILY:**
*Labiatae*

**COMMON ENGLISH NAMES:**
*Catnip, catmint*

**ORIGIN:**
*Europe and temperate Asia*

**MAIN USES:**
*Medicinal*

**PARTS USED:**
*Leaves and flowering tops*

# *OCIMUM BASILICUM*

Another of the many digestive herbs, *Ocimum* is a little different from the rest in that it is both calming and cheering to the spirits. It can help to ease headaches and migraines, and use of the essential oil is said to increase enthusiasm. Pretty close to pure essence of sunshine, it is a lovely herb to use in the winter when your spirits are low.

## Culinary

Prized at least since classical times for its wonderful flavour, *Ocimum* is used in all sorts of cooking traditions, from Thai — as an ingredient of some fragrant spiced dishes — to Italian — as in pesto sauce. In Europe it has most often been used with tomatoes, both cooked and in salads. It is sweet enough to be used in fruit cups and punches as well.

## Other

Oil of basil is used in the perfumery and liquor industries.

## Cultivation

*Ocimum* is easy to grow from seed, but very tender — both to frost and to slugs. Away from its native latitude, it is an indoor herb, needing rich soil and plenty of sunshine. Picking the leaves continuously will encourage more to be produced, and as this is one herb that is far better fresh than dried.

There are several cultivars, including a purple and a lemon-scented variety. *Ocimum minimum* (bush basil) is smaller and bushier than sweet basil.

**FAMILY:**

*Labiatae*

**COMMON ENGLISH NAMES:**

*Common basil, sweet basil*

**ORIGIN:**

*India, southern Europe*

**MAIN USES:**

*Medicinal, culinary, perfume*

**PARTS USED:**

*Leafy tops*

# OENOTHERA BIENNIS

*O*enothera flowers were traditionally used to treat persistent coughs, but its older uses have been completely eclipsed in recent years, ever since the seeds were found to be a rich source of gammalinolenic acid (GLA). GLA is needed by the body to make certain prostaglandins, which help to quell inflammatory reactions. Oil extracted from the seed of *Oenothera*, either neat or in capsules, has been shown to help eczema, rheumatoid arthritis, premenstrual tension and menopausal symptoms. It also seems to slow the progress of multiple sclerosis. Hence, it has become quite a superstar in the herb world.

**FAMILY:**
*Onagraceae*

**COMMON ENGLISH NAMES:**
*Evening primrose, tree primrose*

**ORIGIN:**
*North America; now widespread in Europe*

**MAIN USES:**
*Medicinal*

**PARTS USED:**
*Oil from the seeds*

## Culinary
The Native Americans ate the young stems and leaves, and this custom was introduced to Europe, along with the plants themselves, in the 17th century.

## Caution
The dosage given on most brands of capsules is from 500mg to 2g daily. This is sufficient for long-term use, but for acute inflammatory conditions like eczema and arthritis, a much higher dose is needed at first — more like 3–4g. Consult a professional if you are unsure about how much you should be taking.

## Cultivation
*Oenothera* is hardy and not too fussy, although it prefers good sandy soil and plenty of sun. The flowers, as its English name suggests, open in early evening. Sow seed in spring, and the plant will flower the following year, and then re-seed itself.

# LEA
# EUROPEA

O lives have always been prized for their intense and stimulating flavour. In addition, the oil is gently laxative, and acts as a sort of internal lubricant, helping with dry skin and joint problems. Traditionally, the leaves and bark were used to bring down fevers, but they have been attracting more interest recently for their ability to reduce blood pressure. *Olea* can be combined with herbs like *Achillea*, *Tilia* and *Crataegus* for this effect.

## Culinary

Olives and olive oil are too well known to need much description, as they are now eaten in most parts of the world. Olive oil is the best oil for cooking because it does not easily break down to form saturated fats like most other vegetable oils.

| | |
|---:|---|
| FAMILY: | |
| *Oleaceae* | |
| COMMON ENGLISH NAMES: | |
| *Olive* | |
| ORIGIN: | |
| *Asia Minor and Syria; cultivated in Mediterranean, South America and South Australia* | |
| MAIN USES: | |
| *Medicinal, culinary, craft* | |
| PARTS USED: | |
| *Fruit, leaves, bark* | |

## Other

The wood of the *Olea* tree is highly prized. It is hard, beautifully veined, slightly fragrant, and takes a fine polish. It is mainly used for furniture and carving.

## Cultivation

*Olea* is a small evergreen tree, which can live a very long time. The trees start to fruit in their second year, and the fruits can be processed in various ways for eating, or pressed to obtain the oil. Leaves and bark can be collected at any time.

# *ORIGANUM VULGARE*

Like all the culinary herbs, *Origanum* helps the digestion, but it has its own unique mixture of qualities as well. *Origanum vulgare* is fairly antiseptic, like *Thymus,* and can be used in the same way for chest complaints, coughs and colds. A gargle will help to heal oral thrush and mouth ulcers. It is also quite sedative, so that it can be used to relieve headaches, calm the nerves and aid sleep. The oil, diluted in a cream or oil base, will relieve pain in the joints and muscles when rubbed in.

## Culinary

An old favourite in the kitchen garden, *Origanum* — whether sweet or wild — has always been valued for its scent and taste. *Origanum vulgare* tends to be spicier, and *Origanum majorana* more delicately flavoured.

**FAMILY:**
*Labiatae*

**COMMON ENGLISH NAMES:**
*Wild marjoram, oregano*

**ORIGIN:**
*Asia, Europe and North Africa*

**MAIN USES:**
*Medicinal, culinary, perfume*

**PARTS USED:**
*Aerial parts*

Most often in the past, it was an ingredient of stuffings for roast meats, or added sparingly to salads; and it was also drunk as a herb tea. These days, it also finds its way into toothpastes, cosmetics and perfumes.

## Other

This was a favourite strewing herb in the Middle Ages, and the juice was used to clean furniture. The herb stays fragrant after drying, and so lends itself to use in pot-pourris, sachets and herb pillows.

## Cultivation

*Origanum vulgare*, as its English name suggests, grows wild, but it can easily be grown from seed or by root division. It is perennial, and can tolerate a fair amount of damp or frost. The flowers appear from June until August, and the herb should be gathered just before they open. Sweet marjoram (*Origanum majorana*), on the other hand, is very frost-tender, and must be sown every year in northern climates.

# PANAX GINSENG

*P*anax comes from the Greek *panacea*, meaning 'cure-all', and that is certainly how *Panax ginseng* has been marketed. It will not cure everything, but it will increase your vitality, improve your physical and mental performance and enable you to cope better with challenges, including fighting off infections, taking exams or running marathons. Sometimes it can help to lift depression and banish exhaustion, and, although its reputation as an aphrodisiac is certainly overblown, it can help to improve your sex drive. This applies to both men and women, but on the whole, *Panax* is a muscular, masculine herb.

Various other ginsengs, such as American ginseng (*Panax quinquefolium*) and Siberian ginseng (*Eleutherococcus senticosus*) are also marketed. Their properties are broadly similar to those

**FAMILY:**
*Araliaceae*

**COMMON ENGLISH NAMES:**
*Korean ginseng*

**ORIGIN:**
*China and Korea*

**MAIN USES:**
*Medicinal*

**PARTS USED:**
*Root*

of *Panax ginseng*, but if you are in doubt as to what to take, consult a professional.

## Caution

*Panax* is not suitable for pregnant or breastfeeding women, or if you are trying to conceive. It can be used continually by the elderly, but younger people should not take it for more than about six weeks at a time, as it can be too stimulating. It is also not appropriate to take *Panax* when you have an acute infection such as a cold; it can help prevent, but not cure infections once you have them.

## Cultivation

Wild *Panax* is now almost unobtainable in its native habitat, and most supplies are from cultivated sources. It takes seven years for the roots to be ready for harvest, and they need a rich soil and plenty of shade.

# PARIETARIA OFFICINALIS/ PARIETARIA DIFFUSA ✛

Certain herbs seem to have an affinity for particular parts of the body, and they can be seen as 'feeders', bringing conditions to their optimum state. *Parietaria's* special area is the urinary system. It is well worth trying *Parietaria* for any inflammatory condition in the kidneys, ureters, bladder and urethra. It is soothing, diuretic, and will help with anything from infections producing cystitis or pyelitis, to kidney and bladder stones and gravel. Try it with *Barosma, Arctostaphylos, Althaea* or *Zea*.

## Caution

The pollen of *Parietaria* is one of the most active provokers of hay fever (allergic rhinitis), so if you are susceptible, let someone else gather the herb for you.

FAMILY:
*Urticaceae*

COMMON ENGLISH NAMES:
*Pellitory of the wall*

ORIGIN:
*Southern and Western Europe*

MAIN USES:
*Medicinal*

PARTS USED:
*Aerial parts*

## Cultivation

*Parietaria* is very common, growing on walls and in stony places throughout its habitat. Collect the leaves and stems between June and September.

# PASSIFLORA INCARNATA

Some herbs give clues to their virtues in their names. Passion flower does the opposite; rather than raising fire, it helps to calm it down. *Passiflora* is the first herb of choice for adults who cannot sleep. It helps to ensure a restful night, with no hangover feeling in the morning, unlike many conventional sleeping pills. Its sedative quality also makes it useful for those suffering from anxiety attacks and nervousness. Try it with *Scutellaria, Humulus, Eschscholzia* or *Lactuca*. In any situation where stress is a factor, *Passiflora* may be worth trying. Take it last thing at night for insomnia, or regularly during the day for nervous problems.

   *Passiflora* is antispasmodic and slightly painkilling, and can be used to help manage illnesses like Parkinson's disease or mild epilepsy, to reduce the pain of neuralgia and shingles and to reduce the physical and emotional tension that comes with asthma.

**FAMILY:**
*Passifloraceae*

**COMMON ENGLISH NAMES:**
*Passion flower, granadilla*

**ORIGIN:**
*Virginia*

**MAIN USES:**
*Medicinal, culinary*

**PARTS USED:**
*Leaves*

## Culinary

The fruits of some varieties of *Passiflora* are both edible and delicious. They are eaten raw, prepared in many ways, and can be juiced.

## Cultivation

*Passiflora* can be cultivated outside its native habitat as long as it gets some protection from wind and frost, although the fruit may not ripen. It is a climbing plant, valued in the garden for its beautiful

flowers. These give the plant its common name –
various features of the flower are said to remind
people of the passion, or suffering, of Christ. The
leaves are collected for medicinal use just before the
flowers bloom, between May and July.

# PETROSELINUM CRISPUM

*P*etroselinum is another strong and friendly herb, whose virtues go much further than simply adding flavour to food. The most obvious use of *Petroselinum* is indeed in cookery, to aid the digestion, stimulate appetite and ease wind. But it also has a diuretic effect, helping other herbs that are working on the kidneys and bladder, such as *Parietaria*, *Barosma* and *Zea*. Its third main traditional use is to regulate the menstrual cycle; it helps where the periods are irregular, perhaps because of its nourishing qualities as well as its stimulating effect on the womb.

## Culinary

The finely chopped leaves, fresh or dried, are used to flavour all kinds of dishes, from soups and sauces to fish pies and stews. The leaves are rich in vitamin C, iron, iodine and magnesium, among other nutrients. The roots are used as a vegetable. It is also used to mask less desirable smells, like that of *Allium sativum*, and can be chewed to mask the smell of tobacco and to sweeten the breath.

## Caution

*Petroselinum* should not be used in medicinal quantities by pregnant women, although it is fine to use it in cookery.

## Cultivation

There are several cultivated varieties. Hamburg parsley has large roots; others vary in the shape of their leaves. They are notoriously slow to germinate,

**FAMILY:**
*Umbelliferae*

**COMMON ENGLISH NAMES:**
*Parsley*

**ORIGIN:**
*Southern Europe*

**MAIN USES:**
*Medicinal, culinary*

**PARTS USED:**
*Roots, leaves and seeds*

but once established they do well in partial shade
and good moist soil. They are biennial, so must be
replaced at the end of the second year. The leaves
can be harvested any time during the growing
season, and the roots lifted after two years.

# PIMPINELLA ANISUM

*P*impinella is another of the ever-versatile Umbelliferae, whose volatile oils make them useful digestives, cough medicines, antiseptics and tension relievers – and they taste good, too! *Pimpinella* is less fashionable nowadays than it has been in the past, but it is nonetheless a valuable all-rounder, acceptable to children as well as adults.

Try it with *Foeniculum* and *Carum* as a good anti-flatulence and anti-colic remedy. For bronchitis and irritable coughs, combine it with *Thymus*, *Glycyrrhiza* and *Echinacea*. As an antiseptic, a strong infusion or the essential oil in an ointment base can be used to discourage scabies and headlice. To help an excitable child get to sleep, mix it with *Matricaria*, *Tilia* or *Nepeta*.

## Culinary

*Pimpinella* is an old favourite in Europe and the Middle East, both in sweet and in savoury dishes. It is an essential flavouring agent in many European liqueurs, most notably Pernod and ouzo.

| FAMILY: |
|---|
| *Umbelliferae* |

| COMMON ENGLISH NAMES: |
|---|
| *Anise, aniseed* |

| ORIGIN: |
|---|
| *Mediterranean and Asia Minor* |

| MAIN USES: |
|---|
| *Medicinal, culinary* |

| PARTS USED: |
|---|
| *Seeds* |

## Other

The seeds can be chewed to freshen the breath, and it is sometimes used as an ingredient of toothpaste.

## Cultivation

*Pimpinella* is now widely grown outside its native habitat, but in colder climates the seed will not ripen. It needs a light, dry soil and plenty of sunshine and shelter. The stems are cut in August and the seeds threshed out about a week later when they are fully ripe.

# PINUS SYLVESTRIS AND SPP.

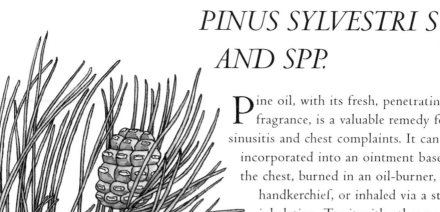

P ine oil, with its fresh, penetrating fragrance, is a valuable remedy for catarrh, sinusitis and chest complaints. It can be incorporated into an ointment base to put on the chest, burned in an oil-burner, put on a handkerchief, or inhaled via a steam inhalation. Try it with other penetrating, antiseptic oils like *Eucalyptus*, *Mentha piperita* and *Thymus*.

Added to a bath or used as a rub, *Pinus* can help relieve rheumatic aches and pains, and its stimulating smell will help to banish tiredness.

## Other

*Pinus* yields a long list of products for our use: resin, from which is derived oil of turpentine and rosin or colophony, pine tar, pine oil and wood. Each of these products in turn has a wide range of uses, finding their way into everything from paint and polish, soap and air freshener to furniture and firewood.

## Cultivation

*Pinus sylvestris* and its many relatives are grown in many parts of the world, and they are among the most important commercial trees. The needles and buds are collected in the spring.

FAMILY:

Pinaceae

COMMON ENGLISH NAMES:

Scots pine, Norway pine

ORIGIN:

Very widespread

MAIN USES:

Medicinal, craft

PARTS USED:

Needles, young buds, sometimes twigs

# PIPER NIGRUM

*P*iper is one of the more stimulating digestives, and was given as a laxative for chronic constipation, although nowadays we prefer less uncomfortable methods. The essential oil, used externally, brings a flush of blood to the area where it is applied, which can be very useful to relieve the pain and inflammation of arthritis and rheumatism, muscular injuries and joint strains and sprains. It works well with other oils such as *Rosmarinus, Cinnamomum, Myrtus* and *Juniperus*.

## Culinary

Used at least since classical times, *Piper's* combination of volatile oil and resin makes it a useful preservative, as well as a flavouring agent and an appetite stimulant. It adds heat to any food, making it more digestible and – in moderation – more palatable.

## Cultivation

*Piper* is a climbing plant, grown around supporting trees. The plants begin to fruit after three to four years, and last about 15 years. The berries are collected when they turn red, and dried in the sun. To produce white pepper, the fruit is macerated in water to remove the pericarp and then dried. This makes it more aromatic than black pepper, and less pungent.

FAMILY:
*Piperaceae*

COMMON ENGLISH NAMES:
*Black pepper*

ORIGIN:
*South India and China; now widely cultivated*

MAIN USES:
*Medicinal, culinary*

PARTS USED:
*Fruit*

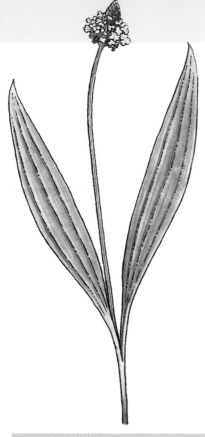

# PLANTAGO LANCEOLATA

Remember rubbing dock (*Rumex*) leaves on nettle stings as a child? *P. lanceolata* leaves have a similar effect; they are quite juicy, and will soothe insect bites as well. Taken internally, *P. lanceolata* is a gentle but powerful astringent, helping to dry up catarrh and restore tone to congested mucous membranes. Hence, it can be taken for any catarrhal complaint, with herbs like *Thymus*, *Solidago* and *Euphrasia*.

*P. lanceolata* also has a special extra virtue, in that it calms down the histamine response that leads to the misery of hay fever (allergic rhinitis). There is some justice in this, as the pollen of plantains is often a cause of hay fever in those susceptible. It works as a first-aid treatment, but if you start to take anti-hay-fever herbs a few weeks before the trouble begins, you can reduce the problem or even head it off altogether. Try *P. lanceolata* with herbs like *Ephedra sinica*, *Urtica*, *Euphrasia* or *Achillea*, or get a prescription from a professional herbalist.

## Cultivation

*P. lanceolata* is very common in the wild, especially in grassland and on roadsides. Once in the garden, it is quite difficult to get rid of, so it is not usually deliberately introduced. Pick the leaves throughout the summer, and dry them fast to avoid discoloration.

**FAMILY:**
Plantaginaceae

**COMMON ENGLISH NAMES:**
Plantain, ribwort

**ORIGIN:**
Europe, Northern and Central Asia

**MAIN USES:**
Medicinal

**PARTS USED:**
Leaves

# PLANTAGO PSYLLIUM

Like Linseed (*Linum usitatissimum*), the seeds of *Plantago psyllium* are one of our most useful herbal bulk laxatives. They are very rich in mucilage, and will absorb many times their volume of water when soaked. Two to three teaspoonfuls swallowed with a glass of water will help to stimulate peristalsis in the gut, leading to a good bowel movement without the need for the more irritating laxatives. It is more of a normaliser than a laxative, in fact, as it will also help to slow down the diarrhoea that can result from irritable bowel and colitis. The dosage is only a guideline, as there is no danger of overdose; it is up to you to find the most effective amount, and the best time of day to take it. It may be useful to take some of the carminative herbs like *Foeniculum*, *Carum* or *Zingiber* at the same time to reduce the possibility of griping.

## Other

There are many other members of the plantago family that are used medicinally, including *Plantago major* (greater plantain), *Plantago media* (lesser plantain) and *Plantago ovata* (ispaghula), whose seeds are used in much the same way as *P. psyllium* seed.

**FAMILY:**
*Plantaginaceae*

**COMMON ENGLISH NAMES:**
*Psyllium seed, flea seed*

**ORIGIN:**
*Southern Europe, Southern Asia and North Africa*

**MAIN USES:**
*Medicinal*

**PARTS USED:**
*Seeds*

# POTENTILLA TORMENTILLA

The English name, 'tormentil', comes from the Latin word *tormentum*, or gripes, which indicates this herb's principal virtue. It is one of our most powerful astringents, able to stop diarrhoea, whether it is acute or chronic, and hence to calm down gripes and colic. It is very useful as a first aid, with herbs like *Matricaria* and *Symphytum*, but also worth trying for long-term problems like irritable bowel and ulcerative colitis, as part of a larger management strategy. Try it with *Melissa*, *Mentha piperita* or *Filipendula*, among many other possibilities.

## Other
The whole plant is so rich in tannins that it has been used as a tanning agent in the past in areas like the Orkney Islands, where oak trees are scarce.

## Cultivation
*Potentilla tormentilla* is a fairly common grassland herb, although it can be found anywhere from high moors to lowland meadows, provided the soil is light and acid. The roots are dug in the autumn, and they must be washed and cut into small pieces before drying.

FAMILY:
*Rosaceae*

COMMON ENGLISH NAMES:
*Tormentil*

ORIGIN:
*Europe, Western Asia and North Africa*

MAIN USES:
*Medicinal*

PARTS USED:
*Rhizome*

# PRIMULA VERIS

*P*rimula used to be seen as something of a cure-all, given for everything from constipation to wrinkles, but nowadays it is used in two main ways. It is a gentle sedative, safe for children and adults; it will smooth out nervous tension, ease headaches and enable a restful sleep, and will work well with herbs like *Tilia*, *Scutellaria* or *Eschscholzia*.

The second use is as an expectorant, included in prescriptions for persistent coughs and chronic bronchitis; try it with *Glycyrrhiza*, *Hyssopus* or *Inula*. It is best for a cough that keeps you awake at night.

## Culinary

Cowslip wine is an old country favourite, but traditionally it was also used in many other ways. The leaves can be cooked or used in salads, and the flowers can be eaten fresh, candied or made into tea.

## Other

Other members of the primula family, especially *Primula veris* (primrose) are also used medicinally.

## Cultivation

In areas such as the chalk downs of south-eastern England, cowslips grow in great swathes. However, loss of habitat and over-collection have led to a serious decline in numbers. Do not collect it from the wild; it is not hard to grow in the garden, although it will do best on a chalk soil. The flowers are gathered between March and May, and the roots dug up either before flowering or in the autumn.

**FAMILY:**
*Primulaceae*

**COMMON ENGLISH NAMES:**
*Cowslip, paigle*

**ORIGIN:**
*Europe and temperate Asia*

**MAIN USES:**
*Medicinal, culinary*

**PARTS USED:**
*Flowers and root*

# PRUNUS SEROTINA

The special virtue of *Prunus serotina* is that it inhibits the cough reflex. This makes it very handy when you have an irritating cough, but it should be used with care. If the cough is simply a response to a sore throat, an allergic reaction, or a tickle, then suppressing it will do no harm. If, however, the cough is an attempt to clear mucus from the lungs or bronchi, then to hinder it is a mistake, and may lead to greater problems. Be sure that the cough is unproductive before using *Prunus*.

Prunus can play a valuable role in the easing of whooping cough and asthma. Try it with *Glycyrrhiza*, *Inula* and *Primula*.

## Other

The wood has a fine grain and polishes well, making it a popular choice for cabinetmakers and woodcarvers.

## Cultivation

The bark is collected from young plants in the autumn, and just the inner bark dried for use.

FAMILY:
*Rosaceae*

COMMON ENGLISH NAMES:
Wild cherry

ORIGIN:
North America

MAIN USES:
Medicinal, craft

PARTS USED:
Bark

# RHEUM PALMATUM

In large doses, *Rheum* is one of our safest and most effective laxatives, clearing the bowels without creating dependency and further constipation, unlike some of the more stimulating laxatives. Use it with carminative herbs like *Foeniculum, Carum* or *Elettaria* – there are plenty to choose from – to relieve any griping that may occur. To make a decoction, add half to one teaspoonful of *Rheum* to 250ml water, bring to the boil and simmer for 10 minutes. Add the other herbs and let the mixture sit for five minutes before straining. Drink the remedy morning and evening.

In small doses, however, *Rheum* has the opposite effect. It can calm down loose bowels and ease diarrhoea. This may seem contradictory, but it is simply because *Rheum* is very astringent (also true of its domesticated cousin, *Rheum rhaponticum*, unless it is soaked in water before cooking) and, in small quantities, it is this characteristic that is brought out. In the larger dose, the astringency is

**FAMILY:**
*Polygonaceae*

**COMMON ENGLISH NAMES:**
*Rhubarb, turkey rhubarb*

**ORIGIN:**
*Western and North-western China and Tibet*

**MAIN USES:**
*Medicinal*

**PARTS USED:**
*Rhizome*

overwhelmed by its purgative action, though it still acts to discourage infection and inflammation while cleansing the bowels. A small dose would be just a pinch of powdered root, perhaps mixed with herbs like *Symphytum*, *Calendula* or *Potentilla*.

## Culinary

*Rheum palmatum* is not suitable for eating. It is its close cousin, *Rheum rhaponticum* (English or garden rhubarb) that is grown for its greenish red edible stems. These must be cooked and sweetened, and are mainly used to make desserts and conserves.

## Caution

The use of *Rheum* root may colour the urine yellow or red. Only the roots are used; the leaves are poisonous.

## Cultivation

*Rheum* can be cultivated, but is still collected from the wild for medicinal use. The roots are dug when the plants are at least six years old.

# ROSA CANINA AND SPP.

Rosehips are one of the richest sources of vitamin C, which helps the body to resist infection, especially colds and influenza. They are also high in calcium, phosphorus and iron, giving them astringent and tonic properties. A tincture or syrup made from them can be taken through the winter and into the next spring, when it acts as a valuable tonic. Use it with *Sambucus* flowers or berries, *Achillea*, and *Echinacea*.

## Culinary

In the culinary department, it is *Rosa canina's* many cultivated relatives that come into their own. Rose petals, especially red ones, can be candied, used to make a refreshing and relaxing tea, made into rose water and rose vinegar, and put into cakes, jams and wines.

## Other

People have always loved the fragrance of the rose. Rose oil is one of the most precious and expensive

**FAMILY:**
*Rosaceae*

**COMMON ENGLISH NAMES:**
*Wild rose, dog rose, briar rose*

**ORIGIN:**
*Probably Persia; naturalised in temperate zones, worldwide*

**MAIN USES:**
*Medicinal, culinary, perfume*

**PARTS USED:**
*Fruit (hips) and seeds*

of all the essential oils, valued by perfumers and aromatherapists alike. Rose oil and rose water are used in many cosmetics and household products, and rose petals – especially red ones – are favourite ingredients of pot-pourri.

## Cultivation

The many varieties of garden roses need no description here, and their cultivation has become a fine art. The wild rose, however, is easy to grow, and can be trained through a hedge or over a fence or wall. It blooms in June, and the flowers vary in colour from almost white to deep pink. The hips are collected in the autumn, when they are red and fully ripe, but before the frosts.

# *ROSMARINUS OFFICINALIS*

*R*osmarinus gives a wake-up call, on all sorts of levels. Besides its well-known digestive properties, *Rosmarinus* is stimulating both to the circulation and to the nervous system. This gives it particular virtue in dealing with any problems to do with the head, from headaches, falling hair and premature baldness to sleepiness, confusion, absent-mindedness and depression. It brings focus and clarity and dispels fogginess. Use it with *Lavandula* and *Stachys* for headaches, with *Panax* or *Artemisia* for lack of alertness and mental energy, and with *Hypericum*, *Scutellaria* and *Avena* for depression.

Oil of *Rosmarinus* can be rubbed into the head to counteract hair loss, as it stimulates the hair follicles. It is a useful warming and anti-inflammatory oil, and can be combined with *Juniperus*, *Myrtus* and *Cinnamonum*, among others, for the relief of rheumatic aches and pains.

## Other
*Rosmarinus* is one of the ingredients of eau-de-cologne. It is also often used in shampoos and hair tonics.

## Caution
Because of its stimulating nature, *Rosmarinus* is not appropriate for people with high blood pressure.

## Cultivation
*Rosmarinus* is usually propagated from cuttings taken in August. Like most Mediterranean herbs, it thrives

| | |
|---|---|
| **FAMILY:** | |
| *Labiatae* | |

| | |
|---|---|
| **COMMON ENGLISH NAMES:** | |
| *Rosemary* | |

| | |
|---|---|
| **ORIGIN:** | |
| *Mediterranean* | |

| | |
|---|---|
| **MAIN USES:** | |
| *Medicinal, culinary, perfume* | |

| | |
|---|---|
| **PARTS USED:** | |
| *Leaves and twigs* | |

in a light, well-drained soil and plenty of sun. Too much damp and frost may kill it, but in a sheltered spot, it will last many years and reach an impressive size – up to 2 metres in height. Collect the leaves throughout the summer, before and during flowering time, which is from June to July in colder climates, and longer in warmer ones.

# RUBUS IDAEUS

*Rubus* is a gentle digestive tonic, astringent and soothing for upset stomachs, mouth ulcers and inflamed gums. However, it is best known as a friend to expectant mothers. It tones and strengthens the muscles of the uterus, helping them to reach peak condition for the birth; hence its reputation for bringing about a quick and easy labour. It may not always be able to achieve that, since other factors — such as the position of the baby — also come into play, but it will help the contractions to be efficient ones. It will also help the uterus to return to its normal size after childbirth.

FAMILY:
*Rosaceae*

COMMON ENGLISH NAMES:
*Raspberry leaf*

ORIGIN:
*Europe and Asia*

MAIN USES:
*Medicinal, culinary*

PARTS USED:
*Leaves*

For maximum effect, start taking *Rubus* three months or so before the baby is due; you could combine it with gentle relaxing and digestive herbs like *Matricaria* or *Filipendula*. Carry on taking it for up to six weeks after the birth, especially if labour was long or difficult, or if you have had several babies already, to help the uterine muscles regain their tone.

## Culinary

Raspberries are one of the best-loved summer fruits in the northern parts of Europe where they grow. They are delicious eaten raw, or they can be made into jams, syrups, cordials and wines.

## Cultivation

*Rubus* is usually grown for its fruit, but the leaves can be collected at any time during the growing season. The plants are propagated from suckers or layers, and they need a rich soil. If grown for fruit, the best crops come within the first four years.

# RUMEX CRISPUS

*R*umex is one of the blood cleansers, stimulating the liver to release bile, and so helping to ensure that it is working well. It also gently stimulates the bowel, making it a good remedy for constipation in adults and children alike. Try it with *Glycyrrhiza*, *Mentha piperita* and *Matricaria* to persuade the bowel into better habits, rather than forcing it.

*Rumex* has a good reputation for helping with chronic skin complaints, such as eczema and psoriasis, again because of its cleansing action. Try it with herbs like *Trifolium*, *Viola tricolor* and *Urtica*, but be prepared for treatment to take some time. You may get further by consulting a professional herbalist.

The leaves of *Rumex*, when they are fresh and juicy, are the traditional remedy to ease the pain of nettle stings. Rub a leaf directly onto the sore place. If you put the leaves inside your shoes, they are supposed to help sore feet.

## Cultivation

*Rumex crispus* is a very common weed of fields, waysides and waste ground. It is a pest to farmers and gardeners, as its long tap roots are very difficult to eradicate. From the herbalist's point of view, however, the roots are its best feature; dig them up in late summer and autumn, wash them well and cut them up before drying.

**FAMILY:**
*Polygonaceae*

**COMMON ENGLISH NAMES:**
*Yellow dock, curled dock*

**ORIGIN:**
*Europe*

**MAIN USES:**
*Medicinal*

**PARTS USED:**
*Root*

# SALIX ALBA AND SPP.

*Salix* bark is rich both in tannins and in salicin, which breaks down to produce salicylic acid during digestion. The tannins make Salix astringent, which is useful as a digestive tonic, but it is the action of the salicylic acid that is most important. Like its derivative drug, aspirin, salicylic acid is a valuable anti-inflammatory and painkiller. It reduces fevers, eases headaches, and helps with the symptoms of rheumatism and arthritis. There is sympathetic magic here too, as taking willow was supposed to help make your limbs supple and flexible, like the limbs of the tree. Use it with herbs like *Harpagophytum*, *Glycyrrhiza* and *Symphytum*.

Salix helps to thin the blood, and can be a useful preventative for those at risk of blood clots. It combines well with *Crataegus*, *Achillea*, *Tilia* and *Allium sativum* for this.

## Other

Many types of *Salix* are grown for their flexible young branches, produced by coppicing and pollarding. These can be bent and woven into hurdles, baskets and other useful objects. The cricket-bat willow is grown specifically for making cricket bats.

## Caution

If you are taking anticoagulant drugs, consult your doctor before taking herbs as well.

## Cultivation

*Salix alba* grows wild in wet places, such as along rivers, streams and ditches, in wet woods and low-lying areas. The bark is easy to peel off during the summer months.

FAMILY:
*Salicaceae*

COMMON ENGLISH NAMES:
*White willow*

ORIGIN:
*Central and Southern Europe*

MAIN USES:
*Medicinal, craft*

PARTS USED:
*Bark*

# SALVIA OFFICINALIS

*S*alvia officinalis is quite strongly astringent, antiseptic and anti-inflammatory, and these three qualities make it a sovereign remedy for sore throats, including laryngitis, pharyngitis and tonsillitis, sore gums and tongues, and mouth ulcers. Make an infusion, or dilute a teaspoonful of tincture in warm water, and use it as a mouthwash or a gargle several times a day. It can be combined with *Glycyrrhiza*, both for its own virtues and to offset the bitter taste.

S. officinalis has the ability to reduce secretions of all sorts. This makes it the first herb to think of for hot flushes and excessive sweating, but it is also useful for excessive salivation, and can help to dry up breast milk.

## Culinary
One of Europe's best-loved herbs, S. officinalis is a favourite addition to rich meats like pork, duck and goose, as its bitterness helps us to digest the fat in them, and also offsets the sweet taste. It is popular for stuffing all kinds of poultry, and is sometimes used to flavour cheese.

## Caution
Not to be used during pregnancy or when breastfeeding.

## Cultivation
Salvia officinalis has been a garden herb for hundreds of years in Europe, and many of its relatives are prized for their healing qualities in other parts of the world. It likes a warm, dry situation, and will last for three or four years in peak condition. The leaves are gathered just before flowering, in May and June.

**FAMILY:**
*Labiatae*

**COMMON ENGLISH NAMES:**
*Sage, garden sage, red sage*

**ORIGIN:**
*Northern Mediterranean*

**MAIN USES:**
*Medicinal, culinary*

**PARTS USED:**
*Leaves*

# SALVIA SCLAREA

*S*alvia sclarea was used in similar ways to *Salvia officinalis*, but today the essential oil is its best-known form. Aromatherapists use it for its anti-depressive, slightly sedative qualities.

## Culinary

Clary sage has been used in Britain as a substitute for hops (*Humulus lupulus*) in beermaking; the resulting brew packed quite a punch. It was also popular as a stimulating and refreshing tea.

## Other

The essential oil of *Salvia sclarea* is used as a fixative in perfumery.

## Caution

Not to be used in pregnancy. Aromatherapists caution against using the oil while drinking alcohol, as it can exaggerate drunkenness.

## Cultivation

*Salvia sclarea* is a highland dweller by preference, and will not thrive in wet conditions. Other than that, it is not too difficult, and is often grown for its fragrance and its tall flower-spikes, which bloom from June to September. Collect the leaves before flowering.

**FAMILY:**
*Labiatae*

**COMMON ENGLISH NAMES:**
*Clary sage*

**ORIGIN:**
*Southern Europe*

**MAIN USES:**
*Medicinal, perfume*

**PARTS USED:**
*Leaves*

# SAMBUCUS NIGRA

*S*ambucus has been used in so many ways down the centuries that it could almost be seen as a one-herb medicine chest, but if I had to choose one outstanding application – whether for leaves, flowers or berries – it would be for the treatment of colds and influenza. It is a warming, loosening herb, encouraging the flow of mucus, bringing down temperature and relaxing tension. For acute illnesses, use it with *Achillea*, *Mentha piperita*, *Hyssopus* or *Thymus*. For sinusitis, try it with *Solidago*, *Thymus* or *Verbascum*.

## Culinary

Both *Sambucus* flowers and berries can be used to make fine wines, jams and cordials. The berries can be eaten raw, but they are more often cooked in puddings and cakes. They are a good source of vitamin C, and are mildly laxative.

## Other

Old elder trees yield a fine, white wood, useful for making small objects like toys. The bark and the root give a black dye, and the berries a purple dye. *Sambucus* has a wealth of folk traditions associated

**FAMILY:**

*Caprifoliaceae*

**COMMON ENGLISH NAMES:**

*Elder*

**ORIGIN:**

*Europe, Western Asia and North Africa*

**MAIN USES:**

*Medicinal, culinary, craft*

**PARTS USED:**

*Leaves, flowers, berries, bark*

with it, both pagan and Christian, as befits a tree
with so much power for healing.

## Cultivation

*Sambucus* likes a fertile, damp soil, and grows
vigorously once established from seed, root division
or cuttings. It grows wild in woods and waste
ground, often near where people live, both for the
rich soil and because it has been highly valued for
many centuries. Collect the flowers in full bloom,
and the leaves at any time. Harvest the berries when
fully ripe in September and October. The inner
bark is collected from young trees in autumn.

# SAPONARIA OFFICINALIS

In the past, *Saponaria* was used for respiratory problems, and as a cure for venereal diseases, but its high saponin content makes it potentially toxic, and it is not used nowadays. There are other, safer alternatives.

## Other

The saponins that make *Saponaria* a risky medicinal herb are, in fact, its chief virtue. They give it the property of lathering when soaked in water, and for many centuries *Saponaria* has been used as a cleaning agent, for washing clothes, people, furniture and pictures. It is still useful today for cleaning old and delicate fabrics; it will not wash whiter than white, but neither will it damage precious things. To make a decoction, boil pieces of root in water for five minutes, then cool and strain.

## Cultivation

*Saponaria* grows wild in damp places and on roadsides, flowering from July to September. It is easy to grow in the garden, but take care as it can become invasive. Dig the roots in autumn, and harvest the leaves at any time.

**FAMILY:**
*Caryophyllaceae*

**COMMON ENGLISH NAMES:**
*Soapwort, bouncing bet*

**ORIGIN:**
*Europe and Western Asia*

**MAIN USES:**
*Cleaning agent*

**PARTS USED:**
*Root and leaves*

# SCUTELLARIA LATERIFLORA

The common name 'madweed' comes from its old reputation as a sure cure for hydrophobia. In fact, it is one of the best remedies for any problems affecting the nervous system, not just calming and soothing, but restoring and nourishing. For nervous exhaustion and depression, anxiety and panic attacks, through to more physical problems, including the management of epilepsy and migraine, *Scutellaria* is the herb of choice. It combines well with other nervous system healers like *Avena*, *Verbena* and *Hypericum*, and with the more actively tranquillising herbs like *Passiflora*, *Eschscholzia* and *Valeriana*. For premenstrual tension, try it with *Vitex* and *Matricaria*.

For depression, *Scutellaria* would work well with *Borago*, *Hypericum* and *Glycyrrhiza*, but as usual, if you do not get the results you are hoping for, consult a professional herbalist. Herbs can be used alongside drugs, but care is needed so as not to duplicate or counteract their effects.

## Cultivation

Not hard to grow in the garden, *Scutellaria* does well in open, sunny places. Propagate by seed or root division in April, and collect the herb during the flowering season, between August and September.

**FAMILY:**
*Labiatae*

**COMMON ENGLISH NAMES:**
*Scullcap, Virginian scullcap, madweed*

**ORIGIN:**
*Eastern North America*

**MAIN USES:**
*Medicinal*

**PARTS USED:**
*Aerial parts*

# SOLIDAGO VIRGAUREA

*Solidago* is one of the best mucous membrane tonics. For any condition involving catarrh or congestion in the upper respiratory tract, this is a herb worth using. Rather than temporarily drying up the nasal passages, like a conventional decongestant, it helps to restore them. It is healthy to produce mucus when you have an infection, such as a cold or influenza, or in response to an irritation of some sort. What is not healthy is when the mucus does not clear up when the problem is resolved, or if it seems to have no obvious cause. Chronic sinusitis is a miserable condition, and it is nearly always treatable without drugs or surgery. Sometimes diet changes will help. The likely food culprits are dairy products, wheat

**FAMILY:**
*Compositae*

**COMMON ENGLISH NAMES:**
*Golden rod*

**ORIGIN:**
*Europe, Central Asia and North America*

**MAIN USES:**
*Medicinal*

**PARTS USED:**
*Aerial parts*

and specific food allergies. Along with *Solidago*, use *Allium* (in capsules or raw), *Verbascum* or *Echinacea*. You may need to persist for some months if the problem has been with you for a long time. If you don't get results, consult a professional.

The other main use for *Solidago* is for problems in the urinary tract, such as cystitis and urethritis. Try it with *Zea*, *Arctostaphylos* and *Agropyron*, for example.

## Other
The leaves and flowers give a yellow dye.

## Cultivation
*Solidago* grows wild in dry places, such as rocks, cliffs, dunes, and sometimes fields and woods. It is an easy garden plant, not fussy about its situation. The whole plant is harvested during the flowering season, from July to October.

# STACHYS BETONICA

Considered quite a cure-all in former times, *Stachys* is a nervous system tonic, and is useful for any problems to do with the head, from headaches and forgetfulness to anxiety and sleeplessness due to nervous tension. It is gently sedative, but strengthening as well. It works best when taken over a period of time, rather than as a first-aid remedy. For headaches and migraines, try it with *Rosmarinus* and *Verbena*. For anxiety, depression due to nervous exhaustion, and as a pick-me-up after illness, use it with *Scutellaria*, *Avena* or *Hypericum*.

## Cultivation

A herb of hedgerows, woods and field borders, *Stachys* flowers in July and August, and should be collected in July when the flowers are in peak condition.

**FAMILY:**

*Labiatae*

**COMMON ENGLISH NAMES:**

*Wood betony, bishopswort*

**ORIGIN:**

*Europe and North Africa*

**MAIN USES:**

*Medicinal*

**PARTS USED:**

*Aerial parts*

# STELLARIA MEDIA

Made into a cream, *Stellaria* is a soothing remedy for cuts and bruises, but its most valuable property is that it soothes itching. It can be very helpful for any itchy skin condition, especially for chronic problems like eczema and psoriasis. If the itching is calmed, the sufferer does not scratch, and the inflammation has a chance to heal. Try it with *Althaea* in a moisturising cream base. For eczema sufferers, keeping the skin well fed is the first step towards managing the problem. Affected skin drinks up cream like a desert absorbing rain, but if you can keep it moist, acute outbreaks are less likely, and will be less severe when they do come. The base will feed the skin, and the herbs will heal it and help to keep it healthy. You can also make an infusion of *Stellaria* to bathe the skin during acute attacks or add it to a

FAMILY:
*Caryophyllaceae*

COMMON ENGLISH NAMES:
*Chickweed*

ORIGIN:
*Widespread in temperate areas*

MAIN USES:
*Medicinal, culinary*

PARTS USED:
*Herb*

bath, which works especially well for young children.

## Culinary

*Stellaria* makes a good salad herb, or it can be cooked as a vegetable. Like spinach, it shrinks during cooking, due to its high water content.

## Cultivation

There are many varieties of chickweed. It is incredibly versatile, and grows wild in all sorts of places, especially hedgerows and disturbed ground. There is no need to introduce it into the garden as it is probably there already. Collect it from May to July, and use it fresh or dried.

# SYMPHYTUM OFFICINALE

For many centuries, *Symphytum* has been used externally in the form of poultices, compresses or creams for both superficial and deep wounds. It contains a chemical called allantoin, which speeds up cell division, so that anything from a graze to a bone fracture will heal more quickly. Combine it with *Calendula* for its anti-infective action, and you will have an all-purpose first-aid treatment for any injury. It also is excellent for longer-term problems like leg ulcers.

Taken internally, *Symphytum* gets to work on oesophagitis and peptic ulcers, bowel inflammation and piles. Its cooling and soothing properties also help in chronic bronchitis and irritable coughs.

## Culinary

The leaves of *Symphytum* can be cooked and eaten, and are particularly useful to vegans, as they contain significant amounts of vitamin B12, which otherwise is uncommon in foods not derived from animal sources.

## Other

*Symphytum* is sometimes grown as a green manure, to be turned into the soil or added to compost, both for its mineral content and because it rots down readily and helps other compost material to decompose more quickly.

## Caution

While *Symphytum* leaf is perfectly safe to take

**FAMILY:**

*Boraginaceae*

**COMMON ENGLISH NAMES:**

*Comfrey, knitbone*

**ORIGIN:**

*Europe and temperate Asia*

**MAIN USES:**

*Medicinal, culinary*

**PARTS USED:**

*Leaves and root*

internally, the root contains a certain level of potentially toxic alkaloids, and current thinking is that it should only be used as an external preparation.

## Cultivation

*Symphytum* is a robust plant and will thrive almost anywhere, although it likes a degree of shade and damp. The roots are strong and deep, and tiny pieces are enough to start new plants. Once planted, it is there to stay. Collect the leaves at any time, and dig the roots in spring or autumn, cutting them up before drying.

# SYZYGIUM AROMATICUM

Along with other strongly aromatic herbs like *Mentha piperita* and *Zingiber officinalis*, *Syzygium* can help to quell nausea, as well as improving digestion and stimulating appetite. It is also mildly anaesthetic, and is a traditional first-aid treatment for the pain of toothache. You can chew cloves directly, make an infusion from dried cloves, or put clove oil on a piece of cotton wool and hold it in the mouth near the affected tooth. The better the quality of the cloves, the more effective this treatment will be. Old or poor quality cloves will not contain so much oil. Apart from its painkilling action, the intense taste will certainly take your mind off your troubles!

## Culinary

Dried cloves are one of a range of spices used virtually everywhere, either whole or powdered, in both savoury and sweet dishes. As usual

**FAMILY:**
Myrtaceae

**COMMON ENGLISH NAMES:**
Clove

**ORIGIN:**
Southern Philippines and Molucca Islands

**MAIN USES:**
Medicinal, culinary

**PARTS USED:**
Flowers

with the carminative herbs and spices, they do much more than simply adding flavour. The oil is quite powerfully antiseptic, helping to preserve food and kill bacteria, and it also stimulates the digestion of those who eat it.

## Cultivation

Cloves are now widely grown, although the best are still thought to come from their original habitats. The flowers appear at the start of the rainy season, and must be harvested before they are fully developed to preserve maximum fragrance. They yield up to 20 per cent volatile oil. Although the whole tree is strongly aromatic, it is the flowers that are most used in both cooking and medicine.

# TANACETUM PARTHENIUM/ CHRYSANTHEMUM PARTHENIUM

The traditional uses of *Tanacetum* were to reduce fevers, and as an anti-inflammatory for acute bouts of rheumatoid arthritis. However, these older uses have been overshadowed by its recently discovered ability to prevent migraines. Taken regularly every day, it reduces both the frequency and the severity of attacks for about seven out of ten sufferers. The reasons for this are not entirely clear, but it is probably due to a combination of the active constituents of the herb, which are anti-inflammatory, anti-histamine, and cause the blood vessels to the head to open up.

The best way to take it is to eat from one to four fresh leaves daily, made into a sandwich to disguise the taste. Use other anti-migraine herbs, such as *Stachys*, *Verbena* and *Rosmarinus*, as well for greater effect. It is also worth trying for headaches of any sort, and for other problems affecting the head, such as tinnitus and dizziness.

**FAMILY:**
*Compositae*

**COMMON ENGLISH NAMES:**
*Feverfew*

**ORIGIN:**
*South-eastern Europe; now widespread*

**MAIN USES:**
*Medicinal*

**PARTS USED:**
*Leaves*

## Caution

Not to be used in pregnancy. In some sensitive people, the leaves can cause mouth ulcers.

## Cultivation

*Tanacetum* is a common weed of hedgerows and waste places, usually as a garden escape. It self-seeds easily and, once you have it in your garden, it is there to stay. The leaves are best picked before flowers appear, but there should be a usable supply throughout the summer. They are best used fresh, but can be frozen for winter use.

# TARAXACUM OFFICINALE

R oot and leaf share many virtues, but in general, the leaves are more prized for their diuretic quality. They are as strong as some diuretic drugs and, because they are rich in potassium, do not lead to potassium deficiency, which can be a troublesome side effect of drug therapy. For anyone suffering from water retention, especially if it is due to heart problems, *Taraxacum* leaf is worth trying. Use it with heart tonics like *Crataegus* and *Achillea*.

The root, on the other hand, is one of the best liver tonics, both stimulating and supportive. For anyone who has liver or gall-bladder problems, or is recovering from such problems, *Taraxacum* root is a friend to be relied on. For anyone, in fact, who has had a major illness, or had to take a lot of drugs, or has abused drugs or alcohol, *Taraxacum* will be a solid support on the road to recovery. Use it with other restoratives like *Verbena* and *Avena*, or with liver herbs like *Carduus* and *Berberis*, depending on the situation.

**FAMILY:**
*Compositae*

**COMMON ENGLISH NAMES:**
*Dandelion*

**ORIGIN:**
*Northern hemisphere; very widespread*

**MAIN USES:**
*Medicinal*

**PARTS USED:**
*Root, leaves, culinary*

## Culinary

*Taraxacum* leaves, picked young or blanched to offset their bitterness, are a useful salad herb. The root can be roasted and made into a coffee substitute, and the flowers are made into dandelion wine. The seedheads make popular 'clocks' for children.

## Cultivation

*Taraxacum* is such a common weed of grassland and waysides that it is hardly necessary to think of growing it deliberately. In fact, people who prize a neat lawn regard it as a terrible nuisance. Gather leaves when tender and fresh, and dig the roots in autumn.

# *THUJA OCCIDENTALIS*

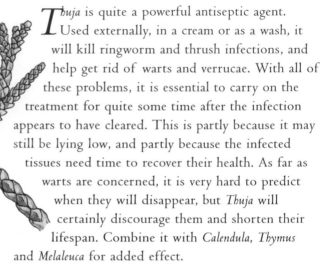

*Thuja* is quite a powerful antiseptic agent. Used externally, in a cream or as a wash, it will kill ringworm and thrush infections, and help get rid of warts and verrucae. With all of these problems, it is essential to carry on the treatment for quite some time after the infection appears to have cleared. This is partly because it may still be lying low, and partly because the infected tissues need time to recover their health. As far as warts are concerned, it is very hard to predict when they will disappear, but *Thuja* will certainly discourage them and shorten their lifespan. Combine it with *Calendula*, *Thymus* and *Melaleuca* for added effect.

Taken internally, it is at its best mixed with other herbs, at a low dosage of no more than 1–2ml of tincture daily, or one cup of tea. It is astringent, cleansing, and helps stimulate the tissues to throw off infection, whether the trouble is bronchitis in the respiratory tract, or cystitis in the urinary system.

*Thuja* is rich in a volatile oil, which contains thujone, a chemical that inhibits cell growth. This makes it useful in the treatment of tumours and growths of all sorts, benign or malignant — but always get professional advice when dealing with problems of this sort.

## Other

The wood of *Thuja* is soft and fine-grained. It is used to make furniture, fences and roofing timbers.

**FAMILY:**
*Cupressaceae*

**COMMON ENGLISH NAMES:**
*Tree of life, Arborvitae, yellow cedar*

**ORIGIN:**
*North America*

**MAIN USES:**
*Medicinal, craft*

**PARTS USED:**
*Young twigs*

## Caution

Not to be taken during pregnancy.

## Cultivation

This variety of *Thuja* is a coniferous tree, growing up to 9 metres tall, and often used for hedging and topiary. The twigs can be collected all year round, but are at their best in the summertime.

# THYMUS VULGARIS

*T*hymus is, of course, an aid to digestion, but that is just one of its virtues. For hundreds of years, it has also been known as an excellent cough remedy, deterring infection, soothing spasm and promoting the flow of mucus. For bronchitis and pneumonia, asthma, whooping cough, and any inflammation of the throat and nasal passages, *Thymus* is the herb. Use it as a mouthwash or gargle, with other herbs such as *Glycyrrhiza*, *Angelica* and *Inula*, take it as a tea or tincture, apply it as an ointment, or inhale the essential oil, perhaps mixed with others like *Eucalyptus*, *Pinus* or *Mentha piperita*.

It is strongly antiseptic action makes *Thymus* useful for all kinds of infections, whether bacterial, viral or fungal. For persistent problems with *candida*, use it in a cream base, and take it internally with *Calendula*, *Thuja* or *Echinacea*. To help cleanse the digestive system after a stomach bug or parasitic infection, take *Thymus* with *Matricaria*, *Symphytum* or *Artemisia vulgare*.

## Culinary
One of Europe's most popular culinary herbs, *Thymus* is justly valued for its flavour, its ability to help digestion, and its anti-microbial action. It is slightly bitter, lending itself to savoury dishes, such as soups, stews and sauces, whether they contain meat, fish or vegetables. It is one of the essential ingredients of bouquet garni.

FAMILY:

*Labiatae*

COMMON ENGLISH NAMES:

*Thyme, garden thyme*

ORIGIN:

*Western Mediterranean*

MAIN USES:

*Medicinal, culinary, perfume*

PARTS USED:

*Leaves and flowering tops*

### Other

Oil of *Thymus* is widely used in cosmetics, perfumes and toothpastes, for its fragrance and its cleansing action. The flowers are loved by bees, and make a fine honey.

### Cultivation

*Thymus* is a familiar garden herb. There are many varieties besides *Thymus*

*vulgaris*, which are grown for variations in leaves, flowers, habit – creeping or upright – and, of course, fragrance. They all have broadly similar medicinal properties, but *Thymus vulgaris* is the strongest. It likes a dry, gravelly soil and plenty of sun, and will last for many years as long as it is protected from too much damp and frost. Collect the flowering branches from June to August. Dry them whole, and strip the leaves and flowers off the stems for storage.

# TILIA EUROPEA

*Tilia* is a gentle but surprisingly strong relaxant. When you feel in need of being held, *Tilia* is a source of comfort. It will dissolve nervous tension, and stimulate the circulation, even to the extent of producing a sweat, which makes it very useful for headaches and migraines, feverish conditions like colds and influenza, insomnia and over-excitability. Try it with *Rosmarinus* and *Stachys* for headaches, with *Sambucus* and *Achillea* for colds, and with herbs like *Eschscholzia*, *Scutellaria* or *Lactuca* for nervous tension in both adults and children.

Tilia is the first herb of choice for anyone suffering from high blood pressure or arterial disease. This is not only because of its action on the circulation and on the nervous system, but also because it has a long-standing reputation for preventing arteriosclerosis, or hardening of the arteries. Use it with *Achillea*, *Viscum* or *Crataegus* for high blood pressure, but if the condition persists, get medical help or see a professional herbalist.

## Culinary

In many parts of Europe, and especially in France, limeflower tea is a popular drink.

## Other

The wood is used for carving, and the inner bark can be used to make baskets. Limeflower honey is one of the finest-flavoured honeys available.

**FAMILY:**
*Tiliaceae*

**COMMON ENGLISH NAMES:**
*Limeflowers, linden*

**ORIGIN:**
*Northern temperate areas*

**MAIN USES:**
*Medicinal, culinary, craft*

**PARTS USED:**
*Flowers*

## Cultivation

Lime trees are common throughout their habitat, not so much in gardens, but in woods and parks, for they can reach 40 metres in height. Collect the flowers, together with the bracts, on a dry day, as soon as they appear around midsummer.

# TRIFOLIUM PRATENSE

The main traditional use of *Trifolium* is as a remedy for skin complaints in children, especially eczema. It is a gentle cleanser, and can be very effective when used with other skin-cleansing herbs like *Rumex*, *Viola tricolor* and *Urtica*. It may be necessary to persist with treatment for some time, in order to strengthen the system, and it may be worth trying oil of evening primrose (*Oenothera*) as well.

Trifolium is also antispasmodic and expectorant, giving it a role to play in the treatment of childhood chest infections, whooping cough and asthma. Use it with *Thymus*, *Hyssopus*, *Glycyrrhiza* or *Echinacea*.

In recent years, *Trifolium* has attracted attention because of its oestrogenic quality. Many plants contain steroids, and when taken by humans or

FAMILY:
*Leguminosae*

COMMON ENGLISH NAMES:
*Red clover*

ORIGIN:
*Europe, Central and Northern Asia*

MAIN USES:
*Medicinal*

PARTS USED:
*Flower heads*

animals these can either mimic the effects of our own steroidal hormones, or stimulate the body to produce more of its own. Women who are having irregular or heavy periods, pre-menstrual tension and menopausal problems because of hormonal imbalances can use *Trifolium*, along with other oestrogenic herbs such as *Salvia*, *Angelica sinensis* (Chinese angelica) and *Humulus*. If a woman has been recommended hormone replacement therapy (HRT), but it proves unsuitable for any reason, herbs can be well worth a try. As ever, consult a professional herbalist to get the best results.

## Other
*Trifolium* is a useful meadow herb, helping to fix nitrogen in the soil, as well as providing variety to the animals feeding on it.

## Cultivation
*Trifolium* is a common weed of roadsides and hedgerows, doing especially well on light, sandy soil. Its fragrant flowers appear between May and September, and should be gathered when newly opened.

# TRIGONELLA FOENUM-GRAECUM

Besides its well-known role as a spice and an appetite stimulant, *Trigonella* is a very useful anti-inflammatory remedy. It contains a lot of mucilage, which will soothe a sore throat, an upset stomach or irritable bowel. Used externally as a poultice, it can help to heal boils, abscesses and sores of any sort. It also has a reputation for healing fistulas and tumours.

*Trigonella* has always been known to stimulate milk production in breastfeeding mothers, and has a strong reputation for helping to enhance the size of the breasts. This is probably due to its oestrogenic action. Those who wish to avoid hormone replacement therapy (HRT) use it to help with menopausal problems. It can be used with other oestrogenic herbs like *Trifolium*, *Salvia* or *Humulus*, but for the right dosage, and the right combination with drugs or other herbs, it is best to consult a professional herbalist.

**FAMILY:**
*Leguminosae*

**COMMON ENGLISH NAMES:**
*Fenugreek*

**ORIGIN:**
*Eastern Mediterranean; now widely cultivated*

**MAIN USES:**
*Medicinal, culinary*

**PARTS USED:**
*Seeds*

## Culinary

The seed is used as a spice in many types of cuisine, and the herb or sprouted seed can be eaten in salads. It contains a lot

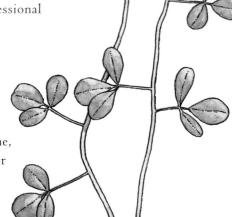

of useful nutrients, notably iron, phosphorus, sulphur and protein and is a very useful food for convalescents or people who are run down.

## Other
Animals like the taste of *Trigonella* in their feed, and it is a useful digestive for them as well as for humans.

## Cultivation
*Trigonella* is rarely found growing wild. It is an annual, grown as a fodder crop for animals, and sprouted for use in salads. The seeds are ready to harvest about four months after flowering.

# TROPAEOLUM MAJUS

*T*ropaeolum is quite a useful anti-infective herb. Traditionally, it has been employed to treat respiratory infections like bronchitis, colds and influenza. Together with its direct anti-microbial action, its bitterness acts as a tonic to the mucous membranes, helping to clear congestion. It works well with herbs like *Sambucus*, *Echinacea* and *Achillea*.

*Tropaeolum* has also been used for urinary infections, and is worth trying with *Barosma*, *Agropyron* or *Zea*, for example. It is a good digestive tonic, stimulating the flow of juices and acting as a gentle laxative. This gives it a place as a cleanser, both of body and of soul. It is said to help clear skin problems like acne, and also to ease depression.

## Culinary

The leaves are high in vitamin C. They have a pungent, peppery taste, but both they and the flowers can be added to salads in moderation. The seeds can be pickled and used like capers.

## Cultivation

*Tropaeolum* is usually treated as an annual in the garden, although it can survive for a few years. It grows easily from seed, and will re-seed once you have it. The main condition to observe, if you want the lovely flame-coloured flowers and not just a mass of greenery, is to starve it. A rich soil will lead to nothing but leaf. It flowers from May to September, and the flowers and leaves can be picked at any time. Gather the seeds when ripe.

**FAMILY:**
*Tropaeolaceae*

**COMMON ENGLISH NAMES:**
*Nasturtium*

**ORIGIN:**
*Peru*

**MAIN USES:**
*Medicinal, culinary*

**PARTS USED:**
*Aerial parts*

# TUSSILAGO FARFARA

*T*ussilago's one great claim to fame is as a cough remedy. For many hundreds of years, it was burned over charcoal or made into tobacco and the smoke was inhaled, sometimes together with herbs like *Verbascum* and *Marrubium vulgare* (white horehound). Nowadays, we tend to feel that the drawbacks of smoking outweigh the benefits, and that *Tussilago* is better taken as a tea or a tincture, or made into a cough syrup.

However you take the herb, it is certainly one of our best remedies for irritable coughs. Besides helping with acute infections like bronchitis and laryngitis, it has a valuable role to play in the management of chronic conditions like emphysema and silicosis, where coughing achieves nothing except to exhaust the sufferer.

FAMILY:
*Compositae*

COMMON ENGLISH NAMES:
*Coltsfoot*

ORIGIN:
*Europe, Northern and Western Asia and North Africa*

MAIN USES:
*Medicinal*

PARTS USED:
*Flowers and leaves*

## Other

*Tussilago* still finds its way into herbal tobaccos, for those who are trying to give up smoking or who use it to relieve the symptoms of asthma, emphysema and other lung troubles.

## Caution

Like *Symphytum*, *Tussilago* contains alkaloids that have been shown in animal experiments, when given in high doses over a long time, to be carcinogenic. However, the normal medicinal dosage is much lower, and the whole herb, as opposed to an extract, is a very different matter. *Tussilago* itself has not been shown to be a health risk at normal dosage.

## Cultivation

*Tussilago* grows wild in hedgerows and roadsides, fields and waste ground. It is not too fussy about its situation and can easily be cultivated if you choose. The first you will see of it are the flowers, blooming from March to May; the leaves come later, and can be collected from May to July.

# ULMUS FULVA

*Ulmus fulva* is a wonderful healer, very soothing, healing and nourishing for inflamed and delicate tissues. Externally, it is made into a poultice for ulcers, boils and abscesses, perhaps mixed with *Calendula* or *Thymus* for extra anti-infective action. Internally, it will heal any inflammatory condition affecting the digestive tract, such as gastric ulcers, colitis and enteritis. It is an excellent food for convalescents and people who cannot take solid food.

To prepare *Ulmus*, mix two teaspoonfuls of powdered bark with a little cold water, then add up to half a pint of hot water, stirring well. Drink a cupful three times a day, or as needed. If you like, you can add a little cinnamon, nutmeg or ginger for the taste and for their healing actions. When treating digestive troubles, taking *Ulmus fulva* alongside other remedies in tea or tincture form is very effective. Try it with *Calendula*, *Filipendula*, *Matricaria* or *Althaea*, to name a few.

## Cultivation

The bark is stripped from the trunk and large branches of the tree in the spring, which usually kills it. Due to over-harvesting, *Ulmus fulva* has become rare in places where it was once common, so it is essential to use only supplies from cultivated sources. The best quality comes from 10-year old trees. The bark is used dried and powdered.

**FAMILY:**
*Ulmaceae*

**COMMON ENGLISH NAMES:**
*Slippery elm*

**ORIGIN:**
*North America*

**MAIN USES:**
*Medicinal*

**PARTS USED:**
*Inner bark*

# URTICA DIOICA

*U*rtica has been one of humankind's most constant and generous companions, and it has to be one of the best all-round supporters that we have in the plant world. A true tonic, nourishing and stimulating, it gives a wake-up call not just to the digestion, but also to the whole body. It is often included in slimming mixtures for its diuretic action, but also helps to stimulate the metabolism, regulate blood sugar so that sudden cravings for sweet food can be eliminated, and sharpen up your sense of what your body really needs. So, in time, and of course with determination, the body can find its own optimum weight.

*Urtica* also has a long-standing reputation for helping skin problems like eczema and acne. This is partly due to the way it helps the liver and kidneys to eliminate waste products, but *Urtica* can help with the allergic aspect of these problems as well. When taken internally, the formic acid, which causes the sting, will help to calm down allergic responses. Thus, *Urtica* is useful for anyone dealing with allergies and sensitivities, whether they are respiratory, digestive or in the skin. It can also help with auto-immune reactions like the inflammatory episodes of rheumatoid arthritis.

## Culinary

*Urtica* is rich in vitamins and minerals, especially iron and vitamin C. The green leaves appear in spring before other fresh vegetables are ready, so it

**FAMILY:**
*Urticaceae*

**COMMON ENGLISH NAMES:**
*Nettle, stinging nettle*

**ORIGIN:**
*Temperate areas, worldwide*

**MAIN USES:**
*Medicinal, culinary, craft*

**PARTS USED:**
*Aerial parts, roots*

was particularly appreciated
in the days before imported
vegetables were widely available. The young
leaves are cooked like spinach, made into
soup, or used in tonic beer.

## Other

The fibre of *Urtica*, like hemp and flax, can be used to make textiles and paper. The roots give a yellow dye, and the leaves a green one.

## Cultivation

Nettles arrive wherever there is disturbed or cultivated ground. On rich soil, they will grow enormous. Pick the leaves, with gloves on, when young and fresh, and you will have a constant supply from spring until autumn. When the leaves are dying down, harvest the roots.

# VACCINIUM MYRTILLUS

**FAMILY:**
*Ericaceae*

**COMMON ENGLISH NAMES:**
*Bilberry, blueberry, whortleberry*

**ORIGIN:**
*Europe, Northern Asia and North America*

**MAIN USES:**
*Medicinal, culinary*

**PARTS USED:**
*Fruit and leaves*

Bilberries, like many wild fruits, are tonic to the digestion, astringent in small quantities and laxative in larger doses. Research has shown that they can help to kill off infectious organisms like E-coli and typhoid bacillus.

A decoction of the leaves, if taken over time, helps to lower blood sugar and keep it under control. With other herbs like *Allium sativum*, *Verbena* and *Taraxacum*, and in conjunction with a controlled diet, the problems of both hypoglycaemia and mild diabetes can be minimised, and the need for insulin sometimes avoided. It is very important, however, to undertake this type of management under medical supervision.

A traditional use of bilberry leaves and fruit that has attracted more attention recently is their beneficial effects on the eyes. It is a long-held belief that they improve night vision, and they can be made into a wash for inflamed eyes. However, recent research has focussed on their ability to heal cataracts and to prevent new ones from forming, and the results have been very encouraging. Try them with herbs like *Euphrasia*, *Matricaria* and *Ginkgo* for maximum effect.

## Culinary

The berries can be eaten raw, or made into jams, pies and fruit yoghurts. They are sweeter than many wild fruits, and do not need much sugar.

## Other

Bilberry juice makes a dark blue or purple dye.

## Cultivation

Wild varieties have smaller berries, but they grow abundantly on heaths and moors, and at the edges of woods, and the flavour is finer than that of the cultivated fruit. Gather the leaves in spring, and the berries in July and August.

# VACCINIUM OXYCOCCOS

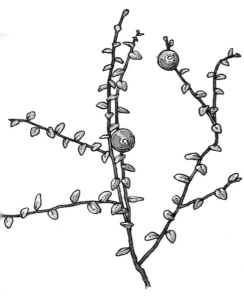

L ike bilberries, cranberries are astringent and tonic, tending both to heal and protect the gut when they are eaten, and to discourage harmful bacteria. Their recent surge in popularity, however, is due to their effect on the urinary system. Most fruits help to render the urine more alkaline, and so inhibit urinary infections, but cranberries are exceptionally good at it. Drunk regularly, therefore, cranberry juice can help clear up both acute and chronic cystitis, and prevent its reoccurrence. Use it in conjunction with herbs like *Arctostaphylos, Barosma, Agropyron* or *Zea* for greater potency.

## Culinary

Cranberries can be prepared in many ways, although they are too astringent to enjoy raw. Cooked in pies and preserves, juiced, added to yoghurts and other desserts, they have become hugely popular in recent years.

## Cultivation

Cranberries are more of a commercial than a garden crop, but they are not hard to grow. They need a peaty, acid soil, permanently moist or actually boggy, and full sunshine. Gather the berries when ripe, in summertime.

FAMILY:
*Ericaceae*

COMMON ENGLISH NAMES:
*Cranberry*

ORIGIN:
*North America, from temperate to arctic zones*

MAIN USES:
*Medicinal, culinary*

PARTS USED:
*Berries*

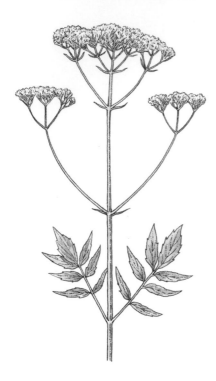

# VALERIANA OFFICINALIS

*V*aleriana is one of our best herbal sedatives, gently calming anxiety and easing muscular tension, acting on body, mind and spirit. It has an instant effect, useful for people who suffer from panic attacks, or who are about to face an ordeal of some sort. Try it with *Passiflora* or *Lactuca* to help calm your nerves without making you sleepy. At the same time, it will help deal with insomnia if nervous tension is preventing you from sleeping, or waking you later in the night. Combine it with *Humulus*, *Tilia*, or *Eschscholzia*, and keep some by the bed to take as soon as you wake.

In the longer term, if you take *Valeriana* continually, it will help to restore serenity and give you more reserves for dealing with stress. It is mildly painkilling as well as relaxing, which makes it very useful for the spasmodic pain of colic, difficult periods, some types of headache, and rheumatic or muscular pain.

**FAMILY:**
*Valerianaceae*

**COMMON ENGLISH NAMES:**
*Valerian*

**ORIGIN:**
*Europe and Northern Asia*

**MAIN USES:**
*Medicinal*

**PARTS USED:**
*Rhizome and roots*

## Other

In the Middle Ages, *Valeriana* was highly regarded for its perfume, and roots were placed among clothes to scent them. These days, the only people who find it lovely are cats. They can get quite ecstatic about it, and once a plant is bruised, it may well not survive their attention.

## Cultivation

*Valeriana* is a lover of damp places by streams and ditches and in water meadows, although it can survive in quite a wide range of habitats. In the garden, it does best on a rich, heavy, moist soil. The flowers appear from June to August but, if you want to harvest the roots, they will be of better quality if the flowering tops are cut off. Dig up the roots in late autumn, when the plants are at least two years old.

# VERBASCUM THAPSUS

*Verbascum* is a gentle giant, its tall spires rising high from verges and waste ground, its strength disguised by its covering of soft down. Both the leaves and the flowers make an excellent respiratory remedy, toning and soothing inflamed mucous membranes. *Verbascum* is a good children's remedy. It is mild-tasting and gently sedative, easing an irritable cough or a sore throat. For adults, too, it is a good herb to use in acute situations – bronchitis, laryngitis or pneumonia, for example – and is also useful for chronic bronchitis and sinusitis. It can play a useful role in the management of asthma.

For an acute problem, combine it with *Sambucus, Achillea, Thymus* and *Echinacea*. For chronic complaints, use it with *Solidago, Inula* or *Euphrasia*.

## Other
The tall stalks used to be dipped in tallow and used as candles. The leaves, with their fluffy covering, make a good tobacco, which is still smoked for lung problems.

## Cultivation
*Verbascum* is quite common in dry, sunny places, fields and roadsides and waste ground. You can grow it from seed, and it will flower in its second year. It likes dry, chalky soil best, with plenty of sun and not too much wind. Collect the leaves before midsummer; after that they start to deteriorate and are attacked by caterpillars. The flowers appear between July and September, and must be collected in dry weather. If they are wet, they will turn brown.

**FAMILY:**
*Scrophulariaceae*

**COMMON ENGLISH NAMES:**
*Mullein, great mullein, Aaron's rod*

**ORIGIN:**
*Europe and temperate Asia; naturalised in North America*

**MAIN USES:**
*Medicinal*

**PARTS USED:**
*Leaves, flowers*

# VERBENA OFFICINALIS

*V*erbena is a herb of many parts. It is solidly nourishing and strengthening to the nervous system, a friend to anyone who has been having a hard time. It will help to ease depression, and restore body and spirit after illness, making it a very useful remedy for chronic fatigue and other stress-related problems. Try it with *Avena, Scutellaria, Inula* or *Glycyrrhiza.*

Like many of the bitter herbs, *Verbena* helps to even out blood sugar, which can play a huge part in all sorts of problems from mood swings and hyperactivity to irritable bowel and migraines. An inability to maintain constant blood sugar levels is one of the stumbling-blocks for people trying to lose weight, and herbs like *Verbena, Allium sativum* and *Glycyrrhiza* can help to smooth the path. It has a useful part to play in the management of diabetes, alongside medical help.

**FAMILY:**
*Labiatae*

**COMMON ENGLISH NAMES:**
*Vervain, herb of grace*

**ORIGIN:**
*Europe, North Africa, West Asia; now worldwide*

**MAIN USES:**
*Medicinal*

**PARTS USED:**
*Aerial parts*

## Other

One of the old sacred herbs, *Verbena* found its way into all sorts of charms in the old days; wearing it was thought to ward off both headaches and snake bites, and to bring good luck.

## Cultivation

There are many garden *Verbenas*, dwarf or tall, pink, blue or purple-flowered. The wild version, *Verbena officinalis*, has tiny flowers on a long stem, but it makes up in potency for what it lacks in appearance. It is common on waste ground, and easy to establish in the garden. Gather the tops in July, before the flowers are fully out.

# VIBURNUM OPULUS

*V*iburnum is a muscle-relaxant, useful wherever muscular spasm is either causing a problem, or adding to it. The most obvious use is to relieve period and ovarian pains and to ease a difficult labour. It can also help to prevent miscarriage by persuading the uterine muscles to relax, and can safely be taken in early pregnancy if miscarriage is feared.

*Viburnum* will also ease muscular spasm that is secondary to some other cause of pain, sprains and strains, internal injury, inflammation in the bowel or bladder, or tension headaches. It can be useful in bringing down high blood pressure where tension is a feature: use with herbs like *Crataegus*, *Achillea* and *Tilia*.

## Culinary
The berries are used like cranberries in Canada. They are quite bitter, but are high in vitamin C.

## Other
The berries have been used in the past to make ink. The wood is good for making small objects like pegs and skewers.

## Cultivation
*Viburnum* is a shrub, about 1.5–3 metres high, that grows wild in hedgerows and at the edge of woods. In the garden, it does well in partial shade. Collect the bark in April and May, and cut up before drying.

FAMILY:
*Caprifoliaceae*

COMMON ENGLISH NAMES:
*Cramp bark, guelder rose*

ORIGIN:
*Europe and eastern USA*

MAIN USES:
*Medicinal, culinary, craft*

PARTS USED:
*Bark*

# VINCA MAJOR/ MINOR/ROSEA

**FAMILY:**

*Apocynaceae*

**COMMON ENGLISH NAMES:**

*Greater/lesser/Madagascar or rosy periwinkle*

**ORIGIN:**

*Major – Mediterranean Europe, Minor – Central Europe and Western Asia, V. rosea – East Africa*

**MAIN USES:**

*Medicinal*

**PARTS USED:**

*Aerial parts*

*V*inca is an astringent herb, with two main uses, for diarrhoea and for heavy periods. Firstly, it helps to stop loose bowels where there is inflammation, as in colitis and diverticulitis. Try it with *Symphytum*, *Melissa* or *Potentilla* for these conditions. Secondly, when a woman is bleeding heavily either during or between periods, *Vinca* can help to normalise the flow. Use it with *Caulophyllum thalictroides* (blue cohosh), *Mitchella repens* (squaw vine), or other uterine astringents, but do take professional advice as well. Excessive bleeding, especially between periods, should always be investigated.

Another useful property of *Vinca* is that it can lower blood sugar and help to keep it level; hence, it can be useful in the management of diabetes. Again, this should be undertaken with expert supervision, as it will interact with insulin or other prescribed drugs.

*Vinca minor* can be used in the same way as *Vinca major*, although it may be a little less powerful.

*Vinca rosea* has had two reasons to be famous in the last hundred years. The first, discovered in the 1920s, was that the plant could be used as an insulin substitute in the treatment of diabetes. Many herbs will help to control blood sugar, and many others will help with other manifestations of the disease, but *Vinca rosea* for a while took centre stage. It can certainly form part of a management strategy, alongside other herbs, dietary controls, and medical supervision.

The second, and more recent, claim to fame was the discovery that two of its alkaloids, vincristine and vinblastine, have anti-tumour activity. They are now used in many types of chemotherapy, especially for acute childhood leukaemia and Hodgkin's disease. They have side effects, notably on the nervous system, and it may well be that the whole herb, though less powerful, is more beneficial to the system. Isolating a single constituent often comes at a price. Try *Vinca rosea* with other anti-tumour herbs like *Thuja* and *Salvia*, together with plenty of support for the person as a whole.

## Cultivation

A very common weed of banks and hedges, *Vinca* is in leaf, and often in flower, almost all year round. Its long trailing stems root themselves and spread quickly, crowding out weaker plants; this makes it a favourite ground cover plant in parks, especially in shady spots. Gather it in springtime.

*Vinca* minor grows in woods, hedges and along paths. The flowers appear from February to June. Cultivation and harvesting are the same as for *Vinca major*.

*Vinca rosea* is not hardy in colder climates outside its native habitat, but it can be grown in a greenhouse or conservatory. Harvest and store it like *Vinca major*.

# VIOLA ODORATA

Violets – as in 'shrinking violet' – used to be a country byword for shyness, but although the flowers look small and unassuming, they can be powerful allies if we know how to use them. *Viola odorata* contains mucilage and salicylic acid, among other constituents, and this makes it a cooling, soothing remedy, gently relaxing and slightly laxative. Nowadays it is used mainly as a cough remedy. Together with herbs like *Inula*, *Thymus* and *Glycyrrhiza*, it makes a good antidote to soreness and irritation, either as a tea, a tincture, or made into a syrup. Traditionally, *V. odorata* was thought to have the power to soften and reduce swellings, including cancerous tumours, and it is still used for mastitis, cysts and tumours in the breasts. It can be applied as a wash or a poultice, and taken internally as well, with herbs like *Salvia*, *Taraxacum* root, *Galium* and *Thuja*.

## Culinary

Violets can be candied, or the flowers can be ground up to add their perfume and colour to various sweet dishes.

## Other

Violets have always been loved for their sweet scent, and used in perfumes and cosmetics. Nowadays, most violet fragrance is synthesised, as it takes over 100kg of flowers to yield 60g of violet essence.

FAMILY:
*Violaceae*

COMMON ENGLISH NAMES:
*Violet, sweet violet*

ORIGIN:
*Europe and North Africa*

MAIN USES:
*Medicinal, culinary, perfume*

PARTS USED:
*Flowers and leaves*

## Cultivation

*Viola odorata* grows wild in hedgerows, fields and scrubland, flowering from February until April, and so stealing a march on the taller hedgerow flowers that come later in the spring. This is too early for bees, and the plant does not set seed until autumn, from a second crop of small and insignificant flowers. Collect leaves and flowers when fresh in the spring, and make sure that they are dry, or the scent will be lost. There are many cultivars of viola, but it is the wild ones that are best for healing purposes. Grow them in a moist, shady spot, and replace old plants with new ones grown from last year's runners to ensure plenty of flowers.

# VIOLA TRICOLOR

*V*iola tricolor has one main use nowadays, and that is in the treatment of eczema and other chronic skin conditions. It seems to work particularly well for children, although adults can also use it with good results. Use it as a wash for the skin, add it to a bath, or take it as a tea or a tincture. It works well with herbs like *Trifolium, Rumex, Berberis aquifolium* and *Rumex*.

## Other
The name 'heartsease' refers to its old use for troubled hearts, whether the problem was on the physical or on the emotional level.

## Cultivation
Heartsease is a common weed. Wherever there is grassland or waste ground, it will find a foothold, flowering for most of the year. Collect plants in good condition from June until August. If you want to grow it, *Viola tricolor* is easy to start from seed, but it spreads quickly and may become a nuisance.

| | |
|---|---|
| FAMILY: | *Violaceae* |
| COMMON ENGLISH NAMES: | *Heartsease* |
| ORIGIN: | *Europe and Western Asia* |
| MAIN USES: | *Medicinal* |
| PARTS USED: | *Aerial parts* |

# VISCUM ALBUM

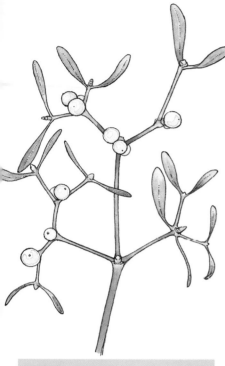

*Viscum* works on the nervous system, relaxing tension and slowing the heart rate while improving the tone of the blood vessels. Its main use is for high blood pressure, hardened arteries or tachycardia, especially where there is an element of nervous tension. It is a long-term remedy, and combines very well with *Crataegus*, *Tilia* and *Achillea*.

*Viscum* also has some anti-tumour activity, and is contained in many mixtures of herbs sold over the counter for fighting cancer. As always, you will get better results if you consult a professional.

## Other

Mistletoe's main use is to hang up at Christmas and New Year for people to kiss under. This custom seems to have started in Scandinavia, where mistletoe was sacred to the goddess of love, and got confused with the old Celtic custom of cutting it for the New Year celebrations.

## Caution

The berries are toxic and should not be used.

## Cultivation

*Viscum* is parasitic on trees, particularly apple and other soft-barked trees, and it stays green throughout the year. The seed is spread by birds, especially thrushes, but you can introduce it yourself by putting sticky berries into crevices in the bark of a tree. Be warned: it will weaken its host. Gather the twigs and leaves before the berries appear in autumn.

**FAMILY:**
*Loranthaceae*

**COMMON ENGLISH NAMES:**
*Mistletoe*

**ORIGIN:**
*Europe, North Africa, West and Central Asia*

**MAIN USES:**
*Medicinal, Christmas*

**PARTS USED:**
*Leafy twigs*

# VITEX AGNUS-CASTUS

In the Middle Ages, *Vitex* was sometimes used by monks to reduce their sex drive. The reason it worked, we now know, is that the berries contain a substance that acts on the pituitary gland and causes more progesterone to be produced. For men, this dampens sexual desire. For women, it can help to regulate the menstrual cycle. Low progesterone can be a factor in pre-menstrual tension, in post-natal depression and in miscarriage in the first three months of pregnancy. It also has a bearing on the mood swings and hot flushes of the menopause.

*Vitex*, therefore, is a very valuable herb for women at many stages of their lives. Whenever a woman is suffering from symptoms that get worse just before her period, such as headaches, bloating, constipation and irritability, she may be responding to the change in progesterone levels in her body. *Vitex* can help to balance things out. Use it with other herbs depending on the type of problems you are treating. A small dose, no more than 20–30 drops of tincture a day, is usually enough, and it seems to work best if you take it in the morning before eating.

## Cultivation

*Vitex* is a small tree, up to 3.5 metres tall, that grows in dry soil near the sea. The flowers appear late, in September or October, and the berries are collected when they ripen.

**FAMILY:**
*Verbenaceae*

**COMMON ENGLISH NAMES:**
*Chaste tree, hemp tree, monk's pepper*

**ORIGIN:**
*Southern Europe, Western Asia, North and South America*

**MAIN USES:**
*Medicinal*

**PARTS USED:**
*Berries*

# *ZEA MAYS*

*Z*ea is a tonic for the urinary system. It is gently diuretic and very soothing, helping to heal inflammation and irritation in the urinary tract and the kidneys. It can be safely used for as long as it is needed for renal infections and other problems, in both children and adults. For cystitis, urethritis, prostatitis and bladder problems, it has both an instant first-aid effect, soothing and calming, and a longer-term tonic effect if you take it over a period of time. It can help children who are bed-wetting, and adults who suffer from chronic irritation, even when there is no active infection to be found.

For infections, use it with *Arctostaphylos*, *Barosma* or *Agropyron*. For inflammation, try it with *Althaea*, *Apium*, or *Alchemilla arvensis*.

## Culinary

Corn is the staple food in many parts of the

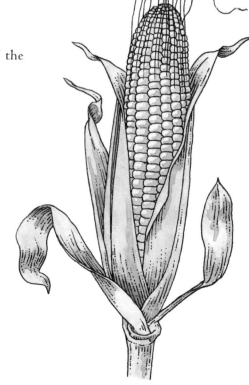

**FAMILY:**

*Graminaceae*

**COMMON ENGLISH NAMES:**

*Corn silk, sweetcorn, maize*

**ORIGIN:**

*South America; now widely cultivated*

**MAIN USES:**

*Medicinal, culinary*

**PARTS USED:**

*Stigmas from the female flowers*

world. It is much more easily digested than wheat, and is also more nourishing; a good food for convalescents, or those with liver or kidney problems. The ripe cobs are boiled or roasted as a vegetable. The seed is dried and ground into cornflour, and used in a multitude of ways.

## Cultivation

Sweetcorn or maize is very familiar as a vegetable. In areas where it cannot be grown, the 'silk' or dried stigmas are easily recognisable when you buy ripe cobs for eating. For medicinal use, the stigmas should be collected just before pollination; the time of year depends upon where it is being grown.

# ZINGIBER OFFICINALIS

One of our most prized digestive herbs, *Zingiber* will help to settle an upset stomach, calm nausea (including pregnancy and travel sickness) and relieve stomach cramps and wind. Like other hot spices, it stimulates the circulation and can provoke a sweat that will cool you down or reduce a fever. In lower doses, it will help to keep fingers and toes warm in cold weather. For anyone suffering from chilblains, Raynaud's phenomenon, or other problems due to poor circulation, *Zingiber* is like an internal hot-water bottle. Try it with *Achillea*, *Tilia* or *Zanthoxylum clava-herculis* (prickly ash bark) for greater effect.

If you put it on the skin, grated into a poultice or used as a wash in tea or tincture form, *Zingiber* will bring a flush to that area, easing inflammation and soothing pain. This can·be useful for muscular and joint pains, period pains and colitis, and it can be very helpful in reducing pain due to tumours and

**FAMILY:**
*Zingiberaceae*

**COMMON ENGLISH NAMES:**
*Ginger*

**ORIGIN:**
*Asia; now widely cultivated*

**MAIN USES:**
*Medicinal, culinary*

**PARTS USED:**
*Root*

growths, thus enabling the patient to take fewer painkilling drugs.

## Culinary

Both the stems and the roots of *Zingiber* are used in cooking, and it has a place in most types of cuisine, either as a spice for savoury dishes, or as an aromatic sweetmeat. It is equally delicious with vegetables or chocolate, and a lot of other things in between. It is one of those useful aromatic digestive herbs that enhance whatever they are combined with, but do not overwhelm other flavours.

## Cultivation

The best roots come from plants at least a year old. Even where it cannot be grown outdoors, fresh ginger root will grow happily in a pot on the windowsill, and you can dig it up when you need a piece for cooking.

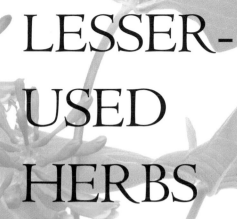

# LESSER-USED HERBS

Included in this section are brief notes on 22 more herbs. Some are used mainly in cookery. Others are medicinal, and of these, quite a few have powerful actions and should only be used by a qualified herbalist. The rest of the medicinal herbs are either less effective than those to be found in the main part of the book, or have been more popular in the past than they are now. Fashions change, in herbal medicine as in everything else, and it may well be that some of these herbs will be rediscovered in times to come.

## ARCTIUM LAPPA

*Family:* Compositae
*Common English names:* Burdock
*Country of origin:* Europe and Asia
*Uses:* Medicinal
Traditionally valued as a blood purifier, *Arctium* can help to clear skin problems like acne and eczema. It can be drunk as tea or tincture, or applied as a wash or cream to the skin.
*Culinary: Arctium* is, of course, an essential ingredient of dandelion and burdock, a traditional drink made in the north of England.
*Parts used:* Root, herb and seeds

## BELLIS PERENNIS

*Family:* Compositae
*Common English names:* Daisy, bruisewort
*Country of origin:* Europe and Western Asia
*Uses:* Medicinal
The main use of *Bellis* was as a wound-healer, used in an ointment. It was also thought to help with liver complaints like hepatitis and cirrhosis, and was one of the herbs eaten at the end of the winter in northern areas to help cleanse the blood.
*Parts used:* Root and leaves

## CAULOPHYLLUM THALICTROIDES

*Common English names:* Blue cohosh
*Country of origin:* USA and Canada
*Uses:* Medicinal
Blue cohosh is used by herbalists in two ways, both related to its virtues as a uterine tonic. The first is to regulate menstrual flow; it will help to control heavy bleeding and restore the menstrual cycle to normal. The second is to help bring on labour when it is overdue, and to stimulate contractions during labour.
*Parts used:* Root
*Any other comments:* Not to be used in pregnancy, as it can cause uterine contractions

## CICHORIUM INTYBUS

*Family:* Compositae
*Common English names:* Chicory, wild succory
*Country of origin:* Europe and Asia
*Uses:* Medicinal

## COMMIPHORA MOLMOL

*Family:* Burseraceae   *Common English names:* Myrrh   *Country of origin:* North-east Africa and South-west Asia   *Uses:* Medicinal
Its main use nowadays is for inflammations of the mouth and throat, such as mouth ulcers, gingivitis and pharyngitis. It will also help to dispel catarrh, colds and chest complaints.

Chicory's mild bitterness makes it tonic to the liver, a useful digestive and a gentle laxative. It was traditionally thought to help with skin complaints.
*Culinary:* The ground root can be added to coffee, to add to its flavour and to offset the effects of caffeine. The leaves, which can be blanched to make them less bitter, are used in salads or cooked as a vegetable.
*Parts used:* Root

*Other:* Myrrh is often added to toothpastes and mouthwashes, as well as other cosmetic products.
*Parts used:* Resin from the stem of the plant

## CONVALLARIA MAJALIS

*Family:* Liliaceae   *Common English names:* Lily of the Valley   *Country of origin:* Europe and North-east Asia   *Uses:* Medicinal
The action of *Convallaria* is like that of *Digitalis*, but it is gentler and has far less potential for toxicity. It acts as a tonic to the heart, and is particularly useful for heart failure, palpitations and arrhythmias.
*Parts used:* Aerial parts
*Any other comments: Convallaria* is a restricted herb, and should only be used as prescribed by a professional herbalist.

## CROCUS SATIVUS

*Family:* Iridaceae   *Common English names:* Saffron, saffron crocus
*Country of origin:* Asia Minor   *Uses:* Medicinal
Digestive and circulatory stimulant
*Culinary:* Saffron is highly prized for the rich yellow colour and warm fragrance that it gives to many dishes, especially paella, risotto milanese and bouillabaisse. It is also widely used in Indian cuisine.
*Other:* Before the advent of synthetic dyes, the yellow colour that saffron yields was widely regarded as the best.
*Parts used:* Flower pistils

## CYMBOPOGON CITRATES

*Family:* Poaceae (Gramineae)   *Common English names:* Lemongrass
*Country of origin:* India   *Uses:* Medicinal
Cymbopogon is used as a whole herb in traditional Indian medicine for infections and fevers. However, it is much more widely used as an essential oil, applied externally. It helps soothe irritations and infections of the skin, and will repel insects. It can ease muscular aches and pains, and is gently sedative to the nervous system.
*Culinary:* Highly prized for its lemony flavour in Thai and other oriental cookery, *Cymbopogon* is now widely used worldwide.
*Other:* It is extensively used in cosmetics and perfumes.
*Parts used:* Stems and leaves

## HYDRASTIS CANADENSIS

*Family:* Ranunculaceae
*Common English names:* Golden Seal
*Country of origin:* Canada and the eastern United States   *Uses:* Medicinal
Hydrastis is an excellent remedy for chronic catarrh and sinusitis. It is
astringent to mucous membranes, in the digestive system as well as the
respiratory system, so it can be useful in cases of chronic diarrhoea and colitis
as well. Used as an ointment, it can help to heal haemorrhoids.
*Parts used:* Root
*Any other comments:* Hydrastis has become very rare in the wild because of over-
harvesting. Never buy it unless you are sure it comes from a cultivated crop.
Not to be used in pregnancy.

## JASMINUM OFFICINALE

*Family:* Oleaceae   *Common English names:* Jasmine, jessamine
*Country of origin:* Northern India, West Asia   *Uses:* Medicinal
Jasminum is mainly used as an essential oil. It is a wonderful mood-lightener,
helping to ease stress and lift depression. Useful for those suffering from
apathy or listlessness.
*Other:* Oil of jasmine is an essential ingredient of many perfumes and cosmetics
*Parts used:* Flowers

## LAMIUM ALBUM

*Family:* Labiatae   *Common English names:*
White dead nettle, archangel
*Country of origin:* Europe, the
Himalayas and Japan
*Uses:* Medicinal
*Lamium* has been used in many ways,
but modern herbalists value it chiefly
for its ability to regulate the
menstrual cycle. It will help to reduce
excessive bleeding and leucorrhoea,
and acts as a general tonic to the
reproductive system.
*Parts used:* Aerial parts

## LEVISTICUM OFFICINALE

*Family:* Umbelliferae
*Common English names:* Lovage
*Country of origin:* Europe
*Uses:* Medicinal
*Levisticum* can help to support a weak digestion. It is diuretic and mildly antiseptic, so can be beneficial for kidney and bladder complaints.
*Culinary:* It has a warm, slightly musty flavour that used to be more popular in cookery than it is now; the Romans were particularly fond of it.
*Parts used:* Root, leaves, seeds

## LOBELIA INFLATA

*Family:* Lobeliaceae
*Common English names:* Lobelia, Indian tobacco
*Country of origin:* Northern United States, Canada
*Uses:* Medicinal
Lobelia used to be highly prized by American herbalists for its ability to cause vomiting, which was seen as a good way to help cleanse the body of toxins. Nowadays, it is used in very small doses, when its calming and antispasmodic properties come into play. It can help in the management of asthma, and eases the transition for those who are trying to give up smoking.
*Parts used:* Flowering herb, seeds
*Any other comments:* Not to be used in pregnancy. Use only under professional supervision.

## LONICERA JAPONICA

*Family:* Caprifoliaceae
*Common English names:* Japanese honeysuckle
*Country of origin:* China, Japan, Korea
*Uses:* Medicinal
*Lonicera japonica* is a traditional Chinese remedy for inflammations, and any condition involving heat. Fevers, red or swollen skin infections, and sore throats can all be treated with it
*Parts used:* Flowers

## MYRRIS ODORATA

*Family:* Umbelliferae
*Common English names:* Sweet cicely
*Country of origin:* Europe
*Uses:* Medicinal
A very gentle digestive, *Myrrhis* is one of the many herbs that can support a weak constitution and aid recovery from illness.
*Culinary:* It has a lovely refreshing taste, and offsets the acidity of fruit when it is cooked, so that less sugar is needed for sweetening. This makes it useful to diabetics and slimmers. Particularly good with tart fruit like gooseberries and rhubarb.
*Parts used:* Whole plant, seeds

## RAPHANUS SPP

*Family:* Cruciferae
*Common English names:* Radish
*Country of origin:* Europe and temperate Asia   *Uses:* Medicinal
*Rhaphanus* is a useful kidney and bladder tonic, and can be taken in combination with other herbs to encourage the elimination of small kidney stones and gravel. It is also said to help prevent the formation of stones, in both the kidney and the gallbladder.
*Culinary:* Radishes are eaten in many parts of the world, and cultivars come in various shapes and sizes. They can be added to salads, cooked, or the seed sprouted.
*Parts used:* Root

## RUTA GRAVEOLENS

*Family:* Rutaceae  *Common English names:* Rue, herb of grace
*Country of origin:* Southern Europe
*Uses:* Medicinal

It is a strong bitter, but too much will cause vomiting and toxicity, and it is not popular nowadays. Externally, it will bring a flush to the skin, and this can help with muscular aches and pains.

*Other: Ruta* was one of the herbs traditionally used to repel insects, and carrying a bunch of it was also thought to ward off infectious diseases.

*Parts used:* Herb

*Any other comments:* Not to be used in pregnancy, or without professional supervision.

## SANGUISORBA MINOR

*Family:* Rosaceae  *Common English names:* Salad Burnet  *Country of origin:* Central and Southern Europe and Asia  *Uses:* Medicinal

Its name, 'Sanguisorba', tells us that it was formerly used to staunch bleeding wounds. It is astringent and mildly diuretic, supporting digestion and kidney function. Externally, it can be used as a wash to tone the skin.

*Culinary:* As its common name implies, *Sanguisorba* is a salad herb. It is perennial, providing a source of green leaves when others are scarce. The leaves are small with a cucumber-like flavour, and can be a useful addition to other salads.

*Parts used:* Young leaves

## SATUREIA HORTENSIS

*Family:* Labiatae
*Common English names:* Summer savory
*Country of origin:* Mediterranean
*Uses:* Medicinal
*S. hortensis* is a useful digestive, calming wind and cramps, and helping to discourage infections. It was formerly used as a mouthwash for mouth ulcers.
*Culinary:* Its digestive properties are especially valuable with foods that can be hard to digest, like pork, cucumber, and particularly beans. Its flavour has been popular for many centuries, though it is not much used today.
*Other:* *S. hortensis* is much loved by bees, and produces an excellent honey. *Parts used:* Herb

## SATUREIA MONTANA

*Family:* Labiatae
*Common English names:* Winter savory
*Country of origin:* Southern Europe
*Uses:* Medicinal
Similar to *Satureia hortensis*
*Culinary:* Again, similar to *Satureia hortensis*, but it is woodier and has a sharper, spicier taste.
*Parts used:* Herb

## TAXUS BACCATA/ BREVIFOLIA

*Family:* Taxaceae, Coniferae
*Common English names:* Yew
*Country of origin:* Europe, North Africa, Western Asia
*Uses:* Medicinal
The leaves, seed and fruit of *Taxus* are poisonous, and not used by herbalists. However, the chemical taxol can be isolated from it, and this has become a useful drug in the treatment of cancer.
*Other:* The wood of the yew tree is very hard, and much valued by furniture makers and woodturners.
*Parts used:* Fruit
*Any other comments:* *Taxus* is poisonous and should not be eaten.

## SCROPHULARIA NODOSA

*Family:* Scrophulariaceae
*Common English names:* Figwort
*Country of origin:* Europe and temperate Asia
*Uses:* Medicinal
A traditional remedy for all sorts of skin conditions, from scrofula – as its name implies – to wounds, burns and inflammations. It is now mainly used, in combination with other herbs, to treat certain types of eczema.
*Parts used:* Herb
*Any other comments:* Some skin conditions will flare up when you first start to use *Scrophularia*, before showing improvement. It may be best to consult a professional herbalist.

# Index

# Contacts and acknowledgements

For information on professional herbal training, contact:
The National Institute of Medical Herbalists
56 Longbrook Street
Exeter EX4 6AH.
Tel: (01392) 426022
Website: www.NIMH.org.UK

Recommended further reading:
Su Bristow: *The Herbal Medicine Chest*, D&S Books, 2002.
A fuller exploration of how to use herbs to treat a wide range of
health problems.

Mrs M. Grieve: *A Modern Herbal*, Penguin Books, 1980.
Still the most comprehensive encyclopaedia of medicinal herbs
and their uses.

Roger Phillips and Nicky Foy: *Herbs*, Pan Books, 1990.
Lovely photographs and a brief history of each herb.

### ACKNOWLEDGEMENTS:
My thanks go to my publishers, Sarah and David King,
and to my family: my partner Martin, who keeps me on
track, and my children, Rosie and Tom.

The author and publishers would like to thank the
following for their assistance:

Plant specimen research: Ena Tuloch
Plants supplied by: Iden Croft Herbs, Kent.